THE SALT WATER AQUARIUM MANUAL

by

ROBERT J. VALENTI

Aquarium Stock Company ● New York

Aquarium Stock Company
27 Murray Street
New York, N.Y. 10007

CONTENTS

TO THE LEGION OF CREATURES CLEAVED FROM THE SEA:
MAY THEY ADAPT TO THEIR SYNTHETIC ENVIRONMENTS AS
WELL AS CAN BE.   (R.V.)

PREFACE

The maintenance of marine organisms in aquariums is of interest to both aquarist and scientist. The aquarist strives continually and at times fanatically to keep marine organisms alive in an aquarium. His aim is to perpetuate and culture the beautiful and fascinatingly odd creatures of the sea in a synthetic environment. The drive to maintain and observe inhabitants from the marine world can become quite compelling. The scientist, while often fascinated as is the aquarist, covers the esthetic aspect of the marine aquarium with a cloak of purposefullness. A biochemist may use marine organisms with hopes of extracting some useful substances beneficial to man or a behaviorist may observe marine organisms to determine the motivation behind defined behavior patterns.

The basic problems of marine aquariums are encountered by all who attempt this endeavor, regardless of motivation. It is for this reason that this book has been written. The chapter topics, while not all inclusive, are aimed at indicating the direction to proper maintenance of marine aquariums. Wherever possible the reader is presented with basic reasoning behind what must be done in a marine aquaria, instead of "You Must Do It This Way" approach. At the end of each chapter is a small bibliography of pertinent reading material. The reader who is stimulated by a particular topic may then, if he wishes, read more extensive material. After finishing this book the aquarist or the scientist should be able to apply the basic principles of aquarium management to his or her specific needs.

ACKNOWLEDGMENTS:

The author wishes to thank Marie McEnery, for her able assistance through-out all phases of the writing and publication of this book.

My gratitude also to Marvin Sherman, of The Aquarium Stock Company, for originally indicating the need for this publication.

INTRODUCTION

The future of the salt water aquarium hobby is indeed a bright one. Maintaining marine organisms under aquarium conditions has been accomplished for many years by public aquariums and a few select hobbyists. Presently, however, aquarium maintenance is becoming feasible for the aquarist. This is due to a multitude of factors, many of which center around technical improvements: for example, new synthetic salts, non corrosive aquariums, better filtration units, and most important, a healthier selection of fish and invertebrates from which to choose. Perhaps the biggest drawback in keeping marine organisms was their poor condition upon arrival at the retailer's tanks. Most fish and invertebrates will adjust fairly well to their new environment if they are in good health, but to weaken them by improper collecting and/or shipping and then expect them to survive under synthetic conditions is expecting too much. Modern means of transportation have done much to aid in transporting healthy specimens of marine life. Many airlines, working closely with importers and collectors, provide styrofoam boxes to maintain constant water temperature, and often re-oxygenate fish shipments to maintain a high oxygen content. Collectors of marine fish have also become aware of the need to exercise more care in collecting procedures, namely, they scrutinize fish for diseases before shipping. By eliminating these basic hazards, the aquarist has only to assume the task of providing an adequate environment for the organisms. The effort expended is well worth the satisfaction of seeing these creatures thriving in an artificial environment in the home. Many readers may have attempted to maintain a marine aquarium by following antiquated procedures which call for maintenance of a spotlessly clean aquarium with a minimum of fish, extensive filtration and aeration equipment, and, of course, a constant scrutinizing of the aquarium and its inhabitants. This author is not able to reconcile the idea that it is best to maintain a "sterile" aquarium for marine fish, when, in nature, they have been exposed to a far greater onslaught of pollution and parasitism than is ever reached in an average aquarium. Why not offer the marine inhabitants an environment which provides their essential requirements instead of an aquarium free of bacteria and algae? This publication will encourage aquarists to simulate, as closely as possible, the natural conditions in which marine organisms are found.

New York, New York
January 1, 1968

Robert J. Valenti

CHAPTER 1

THE MARINE AQUARIUM

The selection of an aquarium will depend mostly upon the budget assigned to this task. Perhaps the most expensive marine aquariums are lucite which are quite impressive even when empty. They are extremely durable, crystal clear, and lack toxic elements. After purchasing a lucite aquarium, one should be prepared to let it stand filled with water for one or two days. It should then be drained and refilled. This step will insure the removal of any polishing substances used by the manufacturers. The lucite aquariums are held together with a durable epoxy glue which, unlike the cements used on metal aquariums, will not crack upon drying. Lucite is a plastic and as such will scratch easily. In some cases it will buckle when filled if the sheets of lucite are too thin or if improper braces are used. If care is used in the selection and maintenance of the lucite aquarium it will retain its new appearance for years of use. Lucite aquariums can be purchased with black or blue back and side pieces, which can be extremely effective in displaying brightly colored fish to their best advantage. There are several types of molded plastic aquaria which are less expensive and well suited if a smaller sized aquarium is the objective. These tanks are rarely larger than twenty gallons, and usually have no seams. They will scratch easily and some of the less durable will become slightly hazy with age.

Glass aquariums have a hardiness factor greater than lucite tanks since they are virtually resistant to scratches. They are amazingly durable due to the use of a silicon, Silastic, (Dow Corning Co.). Glass tanks can be constructed within a few hours, using a few essentials; namely, glass, miter clamps, and the silicon, Silastic. A thirty or fifty gallon tank can be best constructed using 2/8 inch glass, which can be cut and the edges beveled by a local glazier. After obtaining the Silastic and the glass, distribute the Silastic evenly on the edges of the glass; then press these edges firmly together to eliminate air bubbles. The Silastic dries completely in 24 hours. Miter clamps can be used to hold the glass in line during the drying process. After the four sides are together, the bottom is placed on top of the sides; the weight of this piece will provide the necessary weight for a tight bond. Before adding the Silastic to the seams it is better to try the different pieces of glass in different arrangements to get the closest fit between the individual pieces. Once the pieces are glued, they should not be disturbed until the silicon is completely dried; it is extremely difficult to remove the smudged silicon even with a razor blade. As soon as the tank is fully dried it can be moved to its permanent position. Then a final coat of

Silastic should be applied to all the seams inside the tank. This precaution prevents leaks.

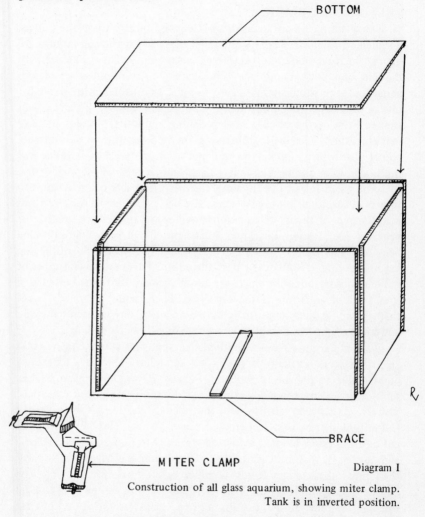

BOTTOM

BRACE

MITER CLAMP

Diagram I

Construction of all glass aquarium, showing miter clamp.
Tank is in inverted position.

The author prefers glass aquariums to lucite since the glass tints the water green and gives it a more natural appearance, whereas the lucite is crystal clear. Unfortunately glass aquaria have one obvious disadvantage in that they are very heavy; for example, a 50 gallon glass aquarium of 2/8 inch glass will weigh about 60 pounds when empty, while the same sized lucite tank weighs approximately 30 pounds. This, however, is no problem if the tank is not to be moved and a sturdy stand is used to display it.

10

Stainless steel framed glass tanks may be used for marine aquariums if handled properly. Many metals will form oxides upon contact with salt water and this will become toxic to fish and invertebrates when present in minute quantities. If such a tank is used, precaution must be taken to prevent the metals from rusting and reacting with the salt water. Here again, Silastic cement can be used to line all seams inside the tank including the metal lip around the top. This step will reduce the possibility of salt water and metal reacting, and the tank should now be relatively safe for marine organisms. The aquarist should realize that when investing finances in the purchase of synthetic salts and marine organisms it is always safest to buy the best; this will insure any investment.

Many other types of aquariums can be used by the aquarist including cement or epoxy coated plywood. These materials are valuable when setting up larger aquaria as the cost is very much less than that of plastic or glass. In either case, by coating the inner surface with one of the many non-toxic epoxy paints a functional aquarium can be had.

The preferred aquarium size should be 20 gallons or larger. Many marine fish will not survive if placed in crowded circumstances. In most cases, the selection of fish for the aquarium will be limited by the tank capacity. This does not mean, however, that you can not keep a marine tank smaller than 20 gallon capacity. There are many aquarists who prefer an aquarium of ten gallon capacity in which they can keep small marine fish or invertebrates or both. One general rule about the size of the aquaria is that height is not as important as surface area. You will be able to stock many more fish in an aquarium that has a large surface area even if the total capacity is low. One should also keep in mind that the finer points of aquarium management, filtration, aeration, and pH adjustments, become more significant in a smaller volume of water.

SUBSTRATES

The type of substrate used for the marine aquarium will be an important factor in determining the success or failure of the venture. Sea water, as will be explained in Chapter 2, should be maintained at a pH of approximately 8.3. The pH of most natural sea water and many of the synthetic salts are buffered to maintain an 8.3 pH. Due to a variety of factors (Chapter 2) the water may become acidic, at which time the buffer will maintain the original alkaline pH. Many times the most beneficial buffer system is the substrate. Limestone chips, approximately 1/8 inch in size, distributed over a subsand filter, are a very effective means of buffering a marine system. The size of the chips permits the unimpeded circulation of water while the composition of limestone efficiently maintains the pH at about 8.3. Calcite chips have a similar function, the major difference is that the calcite is white while the limestone is a grayish color. Coral sand is often used in marine aquaria and it, too, can be an effective buffer. It is better to use a larger grain of coral sand instead of a finer grain, as the smaller size may block circulation of water, and therefore be of little value as a buffer. The use of inert materials such as quartz and silica are not advised as they will do little to maintain the critically important alkalinity. Interestingly enough, many marine fish are found in areas with rough substrates. For this reason, it is no wonder that most of the burrowing fishes quickly adapt to the rough limestone substrate.

Corals

Proper positioning of coral in the marine aquarium is essential. It is decorative and also provides the security of hiding places for the fish and invertebrates. Many marine fish and invertebrates will make a piece of coral or the underside of a shell a focal point of their daily and nightly activity. Amazingly enough marine fish will not be pierced on sharp or protruding corals as will fresh water fish. It was once thought that some corals, the mushroom and brain corals in particular, could be harmful to the environment of the tank. This idea is valid in that the potential danger is the accumulation of food particles in the fine depressions underneath the corals and the subsequent decay of this food. This problem is indicative, not only of one or two species of coral, but rather one which encompasses all corals. Food particles will always collect around the branches and bases of corals and all that is necessary to dislodge the fragments and allow circulation is an occasional movement of the corals. Although living corals have different pigmentation, ranging in colors from white to bright orange, upon drying most will turn white. The color of living coral is due to the pigmentation of the living polyp rather than the calcareous foundation. The white calcareous remnant of the once living coral is often sold in different colors which is achieved by dyeing. Dyed corals can be toxic and therefore it is best not to use these pieces in your aquarium. Coral rock, which is nothing more than coral and calcium deposits, lacks a definite form and is usually obtained in chunks. The island of Bermuda is a big piece of coral rock formed from calcareous microorganisms. Many aquarists use coral rock as a foundation and filler upon which to place more decorative pieces of coral. The use of coral rock instead of corals can give a more natural appearance to a marine aquarium.

Several, commonly used, types of coral remnants.
(Photo credit: Robert Valenti)

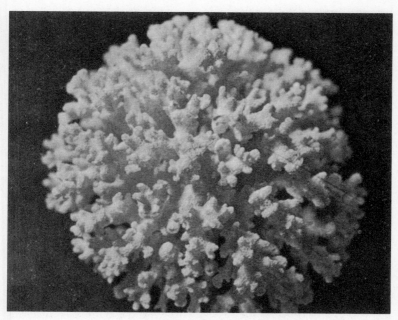

Rocks

Rocks should be avoided in the marine aquarium as it is difficult for the aquarist to tell whether a particular rock has a metal content which could be lethal to fish and invertebrates. It is suggested that their use be avoided. Many aquarists would be disillusioned if they spent $100 establishing a marine aquarium free of metals and then, by placing a piece of rock containing iron ore in it, undo all the effort initially expended. Therefore, exercise good judgement before placing any rock in the aquarium.

POSITIONING THE AQUARIUM

Once you have selected your aquarium and the objects to be placed in it, the selection of a permanent place for it to be displayed is the next step. Avoid areas that are exposed to extremes of temperature, sunlight, or areas containing possible toxins. Therefore the aquarium should not be in a kitchen, near a radiator or air conditioner, or near open windows. The only possibility remaining is a blind corner of the room. In mentioning toxic substances few people are consciously aware of the danger of paint fumes. If painting has to be done near the tank it is safer to use a water base paint and never a lead base paint. Be aware that alcohols and epoxy fumes are also to be avoided. Always place the aquarium on a flat surface which is capable of supporting the tank when full. Remember, one gallon of water weighs 8.3 pounds.

Cantherhines macrocerus, the whitespotted file fish grows to about 20 inches.
(photo credit: R. Valenti)

CHAPTER 2

THE SALTWATER MEDIUM

The salt water medium used to keep fish and invertebrates is the most important ingredient in establishing a successful aquarium. The water must provide the necessary nutrients, specific gravity, temperature, pH, and oxygen requirements, needed by the marine inhabitants. A good medium is one which provides all the necessary essentials and remains stable as long as possible.

Natural Sea Water

Natural sea water is the most obvious medium to be used in the marine aquarium. However, there is the disadvantage of transporting the water from the beach to the aquarium, but for many the proximity to the coastal regions eliminates this problem. Although previous publications have frowned upon the use of natural sea water, this publication completely favors its use. Natural sea water should be taken from off shore regions, approximately 400 feet from the low tide area and then preferably 10 or 15 feet from the surface, so the danger of collecting heavily polluted salt water is avoided.

Collecting and storing the sea water is best accomplished by the use of five gallon plastic carboys. Rather than collect your own water it may be feasible to contact a nearby aquarium or marine station which may provide the necessary quantity of sea water. This measure not only assures easily obtained sea water but water that is free from many impurities. The facilities of a public aquarium usually include a deep well and pump which brings water from depths of several hundred feet to the surface. This procedure eliminates the danger of collecting polluted salt water.

Natural sea water contains myriad microscopic organisms, most of which should be filtered through a fine mesh net. The water should be allowed to "age" in the dark for approximately one week. This will permit time for conditioning of the water. Although there have been many theories proposed as to why sea water should be aged, none have been fully substantiated. It is known, however, that salt water allowed to stand in a darkened container several days is much better to use than newly collected water.

A word of caution to those collecting their own sea water; avoid collecting from bays and estuaries and also after a heavy rain. In both cases the water will be heavily diluted with fresh water and subsequently the salinity will be too low to support the desired marine organisms.

TABLE 1

THE MAJOR CONSTITUENTS IN SOLUTION IN NATURAL SEA WATER HAVING A SALINITY OF 36°/oo

	Grams per Liter at 20°C. specific gravity 1.0279
TOTAL SALTS	36.0
SODIUM, Na+	11.1
MAGNESIUM, Mg++	1.33
CALCIUM, Ca++	0.42
POTASSIUM, K+	0.39
STRONTIUM, Sr++	0.01
CHLORIDE, Cl	19.8
SULPHATE (SO$_4$)	2.76
BROMIDE, Br	0.06
Boric acid (H$_3$BO$_3$)	0.02
CARBON: as bicarbonate, carbonate and carbon dioxide pH8.0	0.026
pH8.2	0.025
pH8.3	0.023

Synthetic Sea Water

Synthetic sea water has advanced through many years of trial and error to become a reliable medium. While not an exact replica of natural salts the synthetic mixtures contain all the necessary ingredients needed to support most marine organisms. Although manufactured under different brand names the contents are quite similar (See Table 2). Many manufacturers, in order to perfect a more substantial salt water mixture, have added trace elements and vitamins which will more ably support the demands of some marine organisms. The standard procedure in using synthetic marine salts is to fill the pre-cleaned aquarium with the recommended quantity of tap water and then add the salts. Since it will take at least an hour for all the salts to go into solution, strong agitation in the form of an outside filter or an under gravel filter is suggested. Once all the salts are dissolved it is advisable to "age" the medium for one or two days. This step insures the dissolving of all salts to make a clear solution. An excellent way to determine if the new salt water is suitable for fish is to test the water's ability to hatch brine shrimp eggs. If the shrimp hatch and are seen abundantly

TABLE 2

TYPICAL FORMULA FOR ARTIFICIAL SEA WATER
(Segedi and Kelly, 1964)

COMPONENT	% by weight
$NaCl$	65.2
$MgSO_4 . 7H_2O$	16.3
$MgCl_2 . 6H_2O$	12.7
$CaCl_2$	3.2
KCl	1.7
$NaHCO_3$	0.49
KBr	0.07
H_3BO_3	0.06
$SrCl_2 . 6H_2O$	0.04
$MnSO_4 . H_2O$	0.009
$Na_2HPO_4 . 7H_2O$	0.009
$LiCl$	0.002
$Na_2MoO_4 . 2H_2O$	0.002
$Na_2S_2O_3 . 5H_2O$	0.002
$Ca(C_6H_{11}O_7)_2H_2O$	0.001
$Al_2(SO_4)_3 18H_2O$	0.001
$RbCl$	0.0004
$ZnSO_4 7H_2O$	0.0002
Kl	0.0002
$EDTA NaFe$	0.0001
$CoSO_4 7H_2O$	0.0001
$CuSO_4 . 5H_2O$	0.00002

swimming about for one or two days this is a good indication of the integrity of the marine medium. After two days the majority of the brine shrimp will die due to lack of space and paucity of nutrients. Most of the synthetic salt mixtures are buffered so that the pH will be maintained at 8.3 after mixing with tap water. If the salts are mixed with an accurate quantity of water a satisfactory salinity of 30-36°/oo is achieved. Synthetic salts also have the advantage of being free of pollutants and harmful microorganisms. This, however, can soon change upon the addition of marine life.

It should be stated that many manufacturers have claimed it unsafe to mix different brands of synthetic marine salts in the same aquarium, since an over abundance of some elements can occur. This, however, can not happen if care is taken that the correct amount of salt is diluted in the proper volume of tap water.

WATER CHEMISTRY

Ubiquitous to marine media, natural or synthetic, are factors necessary to its proper function. Maintenance of the specific gravity, salinity, temperature, pH, and dissolved gases, is critical to the chemical stability of the water. If these five factors are checked much can be learned about the aquarium and its capacity to support or retard the survival of various organisms.

Specific Gravity and Salinity

Sea water contains dissolved substances which give a unit volume of sea water greater mass than a corresponding volume of fresh water. This greater mass or density can be measured to yield the specific gravity of the sea water at a specific temperature. Density or specific gravity measurements are frequently used to approximate the salinity of sea water, although this is not the most accurate method. The instruments used in making a density measurement are a thermometer, (preferably calibrated in centigrade units), and a hydrometer (standardized for 15° C). The warmer a body of water, the less dense it will be: therefore a lower density or specific gravity reading will be indicated by the hydrometer. It is important when taking a hydrometer reading, (which should be done at least once a week) that a temperature reading be taken simultaneously. If a hydrometer standardized for 15°C is used, and if the temperature reading is above 15°C, calibrated tables are employed (see table 3) to determine the proper density. After the exact density value is determined, merely cross checking on the enclosed chart (table 3A) will give the exact salinity of the water regardless of temperature. When one uses a standardized hydrometer it is a simple procedure to correct for temperature deviations which are above 15°C. Density readings on the left side of table 3 correspond to uncorrected readings as they appear on the hydrometer. One merely locates the proper temperature and the closest density reading and adds the intersected number to get the corrected density. For example if the hydrometer reads 1.0250 in water at a temperature of 25°C, by going down the 25°C column and across the 1.0250 column, the place of intersection is 24. This number is added to the original hydrometer reading to give the corrected density reading at 15°C (1.0250 + 24 = 1.0274). Table 3A contains the conversion of corrected densities into salinities. By going down the column until 1.0274 is reached,we see the salinity is 36.8%.

TABLE 3

DENSITY CORRECTION TABLES (15°C)

Temperature of water

Observed Density	20°	21°	22°	23°	24°	25°	26°	27°	28°	29°	30°
1.0100	9	11	14	16	18	21	23	26	29	32	34
1.0110	9	12	14	16	18	21	23	26	29	32	35
1.0120	9	12	14	16	18	21	24	26	29	32	35
1.0130	10	12	14	16	19	21	24	27	29	32	35
1.0140	10	12	14	17	19	22	24	27	30	33	36
1.0150	10	12	14	17	19	22	24	27	30	33	36
1.0160	10	12	15	17	19	22	25	27	30	33	36
1.0170	10	12	15	17	20	22	25	28	31	34	37
1.0180	10	12	15	17	20	22	25	28	31	34	37
1.0190	10	13	15	17	20	23	25	28	31	34	37
1.0200	10	13	15	18	20	23	26	28	31	34	38
1.0210	10	13	15	18	20	23	26	29	32	35	38
1.0220	11	13	15	18	21	23	26	29	32	35	38
1.0230	11	13	16	18	21	24	26	29	32	35	38
1.0240	11	13	16	18	21	24	27	29	32	36	39
1.0250	11	13	16	19	21	24	27	30	33	36	39
1.0260	11	13	16	19	21	24	27	30	33	36	39
1.0270	11	14	16	19	22	24	27	30	33	37	40
1.0280	11	14	16	19	22	25	28	30	34	37	40
1.0290	11	14	16	19	22	25	28	31	34	37	40
1.0300	11	14	17	19	22	25	28	31	34	37	41

TABLE 3 A

Corresponding densities and salinities

(Density at 15oC. –Salinity in parts per 1,000)

1.0176	24.0	1.0201	27.3	1.0226	30.6	1.0251	33.8	1.0276	37.1
1.0177	24.2	1.0202	27.4	1.0227	30.7	1.0252	34.0	1.0277	37.2
1.0178	24.3	1.0203	27.6	1.0228	30.8	1.0253	34.1	1.0278	37.3
1.0179	24.4	1.0204	27.7	1.0229	31.0	1.0254	34.2	1.0279	37.5
1.0180	24.6	1.0205	27.8	1.0230	31.1	1.0255	34.4	1.0280	37.6
1.0181	24.7	1.0206	28.0	1.0231	31.2	1.0256	34.5	1.0281	37.7
1.0182	24.8	1.0207	28.1	1.0232	31.4	1.0257	34.6	1.0282	37.9
1.0183	25.0	1.0208	28.2	1.0233	31.5	1.0258	34.7	1.0283	38.0
1.0184	25.1	1.0209	28.4	1.0234	31.6	1.0259	34.9	1.0284	38.1
1.0185	25.2	1.0210	28.5	1.0235	31.8	1.0260	35.0	1.0285	38.2
1.0186	25.4	1.0211	28.6	1.0236	31.9	1.0261	35.1	1.0286	38.4
1.0187	25.5	1.0212	28.8	1.0237	32.0	1.0262	35.3	1.0287	38.5
1.0188	25.6	1.0213	28.9	1.0238	32.1	1.0263	35.4	1.0288	38.6
1.0189	25.8	1.0214	29.0	1.0239	32.3	1.0264	35.5	1.0289	38.8
1.0190	25.9	1.0215	29.1	1.0240	32.4	1.0265	35.6	1.0290	38.9
1.0191	26.0	1.0216	29.3	1.0241	32.5	1.0266	35.8	1.0291	39.0
1.0192	26.1	1.0217	29.4	1.0242	32.7	1.0267	35.9	1.0292	39.2
1.0193	26.3	1.0218	29.5	1.0243	32.8	1.0268	36.0	1.0293	39.3
1.0194	26.4	1.0219	29.7	1.0244	32.9	1.0269	36.2	1.0294	39.4
1.0195	26.5	1.0220	29.8	1.0245	33.0	1.0270	36.3	1.0295	39.6
1.0196	26.7	1.0221	29.9	1.0246	33.2	1.0271	36.4	1.0296	39.7
1.0197	26.8	1.0222	30.0	1.0247	33.3	1.0272	36.6	1.0297	39.8
1.0198	26.9	1.0223	30.2	1.0248	33.4	1.0273	36.7	1.0298	39.0
1.0199	27.1	1.0224	30.3	1.0249	33.6	1.0274	36.8	1.0299	40.1
1.0200	27.2	1.0225	30.4	1.0250	33.7	1.0275	37.0	1.0300	40.2

The term salinity, i.e. the salt content of sea water, may be expressed as °/oo or %. (For example 36°/oo or 3.6%). Most reef fish are found in salinities between 30-36°/oo (parts per thousand). The salinity of many shallow waters, where fish are abundant, fluctuates greatly since the top layers of water are subject to evaporation by the heat of the sun. This evaporation causes an increase of density due to loss of water. As the density of a body of water increases, the salinity value also increases. The salinity of surface waters will decrease after each rainfall, due to the addition of fresh water. The inhabitants of these shallow zones must therefore be hardy to survive the unpredictable fluctuations in their daily environment. For the above reasons, it is difficult to state a preferred salinity. However, it is advisable to control the salinity so that it is never lower than $28^{\circ}/oo$ and never higher than $38^{\circ}/oo$ with the optimum salinity at $34^{\circ}/oo$ As a precaution against any salinity mishaps, it is strongly advised that the dilution directions printed on the package of artificial salts be followed religiously. After the salt mix is completely dissolved, a hydrometer reading should be taken and any fine adjustment of the salinity can then be done by the addition of extra salt or extra water. Although some fish and invertebrates can tolerate a wide range of salinities, sudden changes can be harmful and should be avoided. If there is a salinity change of $\pm 3^{\circ}/oo$ in water in which a new fish is to be placed, a short period of acclimation is suggested. By gradually altering the salinity of the new arrival's water until it is the same as the aquarium, the fish or invertebrate is helped to adjust slowly to the changing medium.

pH

The pH is a measurement of the hydrogen ion concentration resulting from changes in alkalinity. It can regulate the quantitative and qualitative aspects of a marine population. It influences the isoelectric point of organic molecules and the reaction rates of biochemical reactions. The pH, therefore, can make an environment more or less hospitable for organisms. The pH of sea water is the result of the interaction of dissolved materials such as carbon dioxide, mineral salts and the metabolic by-products of the organisms. pH is not uniform and can vary from one section to another and it can also fluctuate during a 24 hour period. Measurements of pH can be done chemically, electrically, or colorimetrically, the latter being the most common.

Natural sea water is alkaline with a pH of approximately 8.3 and with a lower limit of approximately 7.3. The pH value is maintained by a chemical equilibrium involving sodium bicarbonates, sodium carbonates, and carbon dioxide. As previously mentioned, these elements are abundantly found in sea water. Although the water is buffered, pH changes can occur after the alkali reserve is depleted. This can happen rapidly and frequently since the waste products of marine fish are eventually oxidized and produce acids which cause a drop in pH. The respiratory product, carbon dixide (CO_2), forms a weak acid,

$(CO_2+H_2O$—carbonic acid). This reaction modifies the pH and will lower it. A common occurrence in the aquarium is the decreasing level of alkalinity if fish are kept for a time in the same water. This is a primary cause for death of marine fishes.

The use of calcite or limestone chips helps maintain the proper alkaline pH. This effect is similar to the natural buffering of sea water in the ocean. The chips should be approximately 1/8 inch in size. This size provides good surface area to allow maximum circulation and effective buffering. They should be arranged in a 1 to 2 inch layer over an undergravel filter. In this manner the water will be circulated constantly through the chips and the pH will be maintained. Sodium bicarbonate can be added to marine aquariums similarly to the way in which it is added to fresh water tanks; however, care should be exercised to prevent a sudden change in pH. Many marine fish and invertebrates, though capable of surviving at low pH's (even as low as 7.0), will eventually show signs of loss of appetite and may become less intensely colored. Since a change in pH can grossly affect metabolism, a period of acclimation, similar to salinity changes (see salinity), is advised. The lapse of time, during which the pH is changing, permits enough time for organic adjustments. A small container can be used to adapt new fish to the established tank water, merely by gradually adding some established tank water to a fish or invertebrate in its original water.

Dissolved Gases

When an aquarium is completely covered much of the CO_2 and nitrogen gas is prevented from mixing with the atmospheric gases. These gases are then forced to redissolve in the same water from which they were released. The CO_2 content of sea water influences the respiration of fish by reducing the amount of oxygen (O_2) carried by the red blood corpuscles. In man as in fish, CO_2 forms a non-competitive bond with the oxygen carrying substance, hemoglobin, which further prevents the attachment of oxygen. Since the CO_2 content will also lower the pH, it can be safely stated that increasing dissolved CO_2 can cause stress to fish. The most successful means of eliminating CO_2 build-up in an aquarium is to permit atmospheric air to mingle, unimpeded with the water's surface. Therefore, the top of the aquarium should be only half covered and then either a circulating water pump or filter should break the surface of the water to allow sufficient interaction with the atmosphere.

Aeration of tank water is important, but it may do more harm than good. Bubbling air through the water will accelerate CO_2 evaporation, however, it will introduce another gas, nitrogen. The composition of the atmospheric gas normally contains a high percentage of nitrogen (see table 4). Use of a fine air stone releases minute air bubbles and will eventually supersaturate the water with gases, especially with nitrogen.

TABLE 4
COMPOSITION OF NORMAL ATMOSPHERE

GAS	PERCENT OF VOLUME
NITROGEN – – – – – – – –	78.03
OXYGEN – – – – – – – – –	20.99
ARGON– – – – – – – – – –	0.94
CARBON DIOXIDE– – – – – –	0.03
HYDROGEN	
NEON– – – – – – – – – – –	0.01
HELIUM	
Total	100.00

The excess gas can form bubbles under the skin and fins (See Chapter VI). Aeration not only is used to decrease CO_2 content, but also is used to increase the O_2 content of the water. Sea water is capable of dissolving about 20% less oxygen than fresh water. It has been reported that marine fish require between 0.2 to 3.0 ppm (parts per million) O_2. This varies with the particular species of fish. Reaching a saturation level of O_2 is rather easily accomplished by slight aeration and filtration (See table 5).

Waste Products

Many marine fish as well as invertebrates excrete ammonia as a waste product while others excrete urea which is converted to ammonia. Furthermore the decay of dead organic substances soon becomes ammonia. Ammonia even in small quantities can be lethal to fish and invertebrates. Some ammonia, due to the brisk agitation of the water, will pass into the atmosphere but the bulk of it can become toxic unless it is oxidized by bacteria to nitrates and nitrites. While it is debatable that an accumulation of nitrates and nitrites is lethal to marine organisms, the level can easily be regulated by marine algae. Here then we see the need for controlled bacterial and algal growth in order to maintain a balanced aquarium. The bacteria, which degrade the ammonia to nitrates and nitrites, are usually present on the upper surface of the filter medium and may also be present on the walls of the aquarium. (DIAGRAM N_2 SEQUENCE). Water that has an abundance of ammonia may be made safe for fish by keeping it in complete dark-

TABLE 5

Oxygen Saturation Points in P. P. M.

Temperature °C	°F	O₂ Concentration at Saturation in Salt Water
0	32	11.3
1	33.8	11.0
2	35.6	10.8
3	37.4	10.5
4	39.2	10.3
5	41	10.0
6	42.8	9.8
7	44.6	9.6
8	46.2	9.4
9	48.2	9.2
10	50	9.0
11	51.8	8.8
12	53.6	8.6
13	55.4	8.5
14	57.2	8.3
15	59	8.1
16	60.8	8.0
17	62.6	7.8
18	64.4	7.7
19	66.2	7.6
20	68	7.4
21	69.8	7.3
22	71.6	7.1
23	73.4	7.0
24	75.2	6.9
25	77	6.7
26	78.8	6.6
27	80.6	6.5
28	82.5	6.4
29	84.2	6.3
30	86	6.1
31	87.8	
32	89.6	

Note: Salt water readings pertain to water with a specific gravity of 1.025.

A commercially manufactured power filter showing the proper
return of water back into the aquarium. (photo credit: R. Valenti)

ness for a week. This will, through chemical oxidation by the bacteria,
remove much of the unwanted ammonia. Algae, microscopic plants
which have different shapes and colors, can be grown selectively
depending on the quality of the light source, nutrients present, and the
competition from other algae in the same aquarium. The growth of a
mat of algae either on the substrate, corals, or walls of the aquarium
should provide an adequate population to remove most of the nitrates
and nitrites.

Filtration

Effective filtering of the sea water is essential for an attractive
display as well as to retard and control bacterial growth. Decay of food
particles and feces will quickly increase the number of bacteria in the
sea water and therefore must be controlled by filtration. Kelly (1963)
in his description of the ideal aquarium system suggests complete water
circulation once every hour at the rate of one gallon per square foot of
filter surface area per minute. This type of filtration would be
impractical for most home aquariums and is not a necessity. Many
power filters, which are manufactured specifically for salt water use,
will yield a circulation of 140 gallons per hour, however, the filter units
have small surface areas of 48 square inches. Circulating at this rate

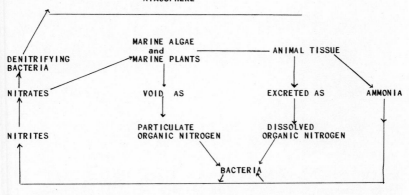

DIAGRAM II   NITROGEN SEQUENCE IN THE MARINE AQUARIUM.

they theoretically need a far greater surface area. (A 50 gallon aquarium having two such filters would pump in 1 minute, 4.6 gallons per 96 square inches of filtering surface. The ideal system filtering at this rate would need 4.6 square feet of filter surface). However, this is not necessary, since one or two commercial filters are extremely effective in keeping the aquarium clean and clear for many years. Therefore a good modified rule to follow is to use a filter of approximately 48 square inches of surface area which is capable of circulating 100-150 gallons each hour for every 25 gallons of water. There are understandably many circumstances which will alter this rule, for instance overcrowding will produce more wastes making a more rapid filtration necessary. If the individual aquarist is industrious, he can build a filtration tank following steps given for construction of a glass tank and use a standard motor from a manufactured filter. Understandably, a large surface area of filtration is far superior to the narrow one provided by present manufactured filters but these, I fear, are here to stay and the aquarist should resign himself to them. If an aquarium of 20 gallons or less is used it can be filtered satisfactorily by a small motor driven filter or a large magnetic filter. In either case the filtration will be satisfactory under normal conditions. It should be noted that the motor driven filters are extremely important not only in effective filtration of water but if the return stream of water breaks the surface it will greatly aid air-water interaction and will increase dissipation of gases. The use of small inside filters, while not recommended, can be somewhat effective in small 5 or l0 gallon aquariums. Once again I reiterate that it is better to invest in good equipment at the start of the aquarium and avoid problems later.

Herald, Dempster, Walters, and Hunt (1962) presented two basic concepts of filters: regardless of filter depth most of the filtering takes place in the top 1½ inches, and the best inorganic filter is a very dirty one, that is biologically active. Therefore, cleaning of filters should be delayed until it is absolutely necessary, perhaps once every 4 months. Once it is cleaned maximum filtration will not be restored for approximately 24 hours. Often filters can be flushed out, using a flow of fresh water, if they have accumulated an excessive amount of particulate material. In this way, beneficial bacteria will remain in the filter box while the excess filterable particles are removed. The filtering material used should be built up in layers of differently sized materials. If a conventional motor driven power filter is used, a thin layer of nylon wool should be placed at the bottom followed by a 2 inch layer of 1/8 inch limestone or calcite and topped by a one inch layer of fine gravel. This way, the upper 2 inches will do most of the filtering work. It should be noted that nylon wool will not break apart as does glass wool. It is possible that fragments of glass wool can be eaten by fish and therefore jeopardize their existence.

The use of charcoal or activated carbons in the filter provides a great deal of controversy. Charcoal (either petroleum, animal bone........ etc.) is capable of removing dissolved gases from the sea water but it is questionable if this binding ability lasts long. It is thought that after a few days charcoal can no longer absorb gases and will then serve only as a fine filtering material. While it is questionable whether charcoal absorbs dissolved gases after being submerged for several days, it can be reactivated easily by drying it for a few hours in a warm oven. Despite current opinion this author feels charcoal is a good filtering material if for no other reason than it contains many fine pores which are able to trap a tremendous amount of debris. Resins or ion exchanges may be extremely successful in the marine aquarium but there is little justification for their use if previous filtering and pH instructions are followed. The resins may interfere with the normal reactivity of the elements in the synthetic salts. The one important result that resins can accomplish, i.e. adjusting the pH, can be done more cheaply and as effectively by using limestone or calcite chips and an undergravel filter. It may be pertinent at this point to repeat that while an undergravel filter is suggested in the marine aquarium it is used mainly as a means of circulating water through a buffering substrate such as limestone or calcite. If marine plants are to be grown, it is advisable to use a smaller undergravel filter. A filter that covers 2/3 of the bottom will not hasten the loss of plant nutrient material, since the plants can be placed in an area not covered by the filter.

No discussion of filtration is complete without mentioning sedimentation tanks. These are merely large water containers in which heavy particles settle to the bottom. The water is then brought to a regular filter to remove the finer matter and then pumped to the tank. Filters such as these work fine if natural sea water is being pumped directly into an aquarium.

The encouragement of algal and bacterial growth in the filter is beneficial as is the presence of invertebrates. The bacteria and algae will be abundant on the surface of the filter and both should thrive without any problem. Keeping invertebrates in a filter box, such as clams, mussels, or some marine worms (Pachydritus pagenstecheri) which act as filters, can effectively aid filtration, however, they should be watched very carefully at first to see if they are thriving.

Sterilization of sea water has been both opposed and advanced over a number of years. The use of ultra-violet light or ozone gas accomplishes the same objective in that they will both kill many microorganisms. If using natural sea water, sterilization results in producing clear aquarium water by lowering the number of bacteria and other microorganisms and simultaneously it may be successful in killing certain prevalent parasites. It has been shown that ultra-violet light or ozone can kill bacteria in natural sea water; however, bacterial infections in natural sea water are kept in control by the antiseptic qualities of the sea water itself (mostly gram negative bacteria in sea water, few gram positive). A good sterilization technique is to use an ultra-violet light unit which is either submerged in sea water (Herald, Dempster, Waters, and Hunt, 1960) so that the water will continually flow over it or position it on top of the filter. The second method is less effective, but will work as long as nothing, including clear glass, blocks the emitted rays. The use of ozonizers to produce ozone (O_3) has been known to the marine aquarist for many years. Ozonizers produce ozone gas by an electrical discharge method. This involves the insertion of air between two electrodes and applying current. The amount of ozone gas produced is greatly increased if the air between the electrodes is dry (this can be accomplished by passing the air, prior to entering the ozonizer, into a desicant column, such as, $CaSO_4$ anhydrous). The aquarist should realize that indiscriminate use of uncontained ozone (freely bubbled into aquarium) will do more harm than good since beneficial denitrifying bacteria will be killed, while it is doubtful that parasites such as *Oodinium*, will be affected. The use of ozone within protein skimmers is more acceptable than direct bubbling into aquarium water.

The aquarist should use ozone or ultra-violet light sporadically, if at all, and only when a tank is becoming cloudy because of decaying waste products. The ozone and ultra-violet light, if used for a brief period of time, will limit bacterial growth and yet allow a certain percentage of the necessary bacterial population to survive. Never aim an ultra-violet light directly on a fish or invertebrate as a great deal of damage to sensitive tissues can result. For this reason, the aquarist is also advised not to look at the ultra-violet light directly since eye damage can occur. If using ozone it should be kept in mind that the quantity to use should be low at the start; 1 milligram per hour of ozone for every 10 gallons of water and if necessary increased from here slowly. Continual use of ozone, except where new fish or new natural sea water are constantly being added, should be avoided.

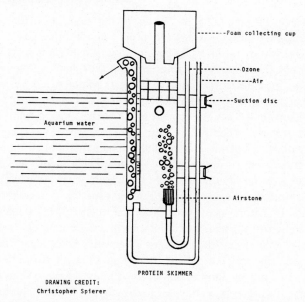

DRAWING CREDIT:
Christopher Spierer

PROTEIN SKIMMER

Protein skimmers, which have been in use since the early 1900's, have become quite popular in recent years and rightly so. They operate on the basis of foam separation which is the selective adsorption of surface active solutes at the interface between a gas and a solution. When one bubbles gases, such as air, through a liquid, a gas-liquid interface is generated around each bubble. When this bubbling is contained within a narrow column, an easily collected foam is produced. This foam will be richer in solutes than the remaining aquarium water. Protein skimmers contain a cup in which the foam condenses into a liquid called a foamate. The foamate will contain a concentrated amount of fatty acids, amino acids, proteins, enzymes and other organic substances. Here then lies the benefit of the protein skimmer, since it is capable of removing harmful materials such as ammonia and growth inhibiting substances from the aquarium water. The use of ozone gas within the protein skimmer in place of air, is beneficial in allowing increased oxidation within the fomate.

Diatomaceous earth filters have limited use within small marine aquariums (under 1000 gallons). This type of filtration depends on passing aquarium water over a porous sieve which is covered with diatom skeletons. The resulting filtered water will be free of most particulate matter larger than .1-.3 μ and will thereby appear very clear. Unfortunately, much maintenance is required to keep these filters from clogging and they are therefore only used for short periods of time.

Lighting

Lighting, of course, aids in displaying your aquarium and its inhabitants and also provides the proper conditions under which to grow algae. Since the most important aim in lighting is to grow algae this should be foremost in deciding the type and amount of light necessary. Incandescent or fluorescent lights will be successful, with the latter being very efficient if Grolux or Magnalux bulbs are used. Grolux or Magnalux bulbs are fluorescent lights which give off light waves in the 450 range. These are the most efficient wavelengths for photosynthesis of plants. The recommended usage for this type of bulb is 2 watts of bulb for every gallon of tank water. The total amount of light one gives an aquarium should be 6 hours daily. It is desirable, if time permits, to have algae growing in the aquarium before introducing any fish. In natural sea water there are many types of microscopic plants and for these plants to bloom, adequate illumination is essential. Synthetic marine media must be "seeded" with algae before it will bloom; this can be achieved by adding a liter of natural sea water to the aquarium medium or simply by adding a piece of algae from a local bay. To attain maximum algal growth it is best to illuminate the tank for six hours daily, using either incandescent or fluorescent bulbs.

Incandescent lamps will grow algae faster than most types of light and, as such, are desirable. Unfortunately, incandescent bulbs have a disadvantage in that they warm the aquarium water considerably, especially in a ten gallon or smaller aquarium.

Contrary to popular thought, colored glass filters between light source and aquarium will do nothing to provide different wavelengths of light. This can be altered by using different types of bulbs. The Grolux or Magnalux, as mentioned previously, yield the necessary blue wavelengths while most of the other fluorescents will be in the yellow-red zone and as such will do little to grow algae. In nature, sea water absorbs light differentially by eliminating the reds and the yellows until at 65 feet very little but green and blue wavelengths are left. The type of available light will influence not only the quantitative algal growth, but also the specific algae growing in an area (Table 6). No matter what type of lighting is provided, it is important to realize that while algal growth is essential, too much light can cause temporary or even permanent damage to the eyes of some fish. Consider that many aquarium species of fish are found at depths of fifty feet or deeper where little, if any, light penetrates. Even species frequenting shallow reefs do not inhabit there constantly. Those families most susceptible to overexposure of light are Holocentridae (squirrel fish), and Scorpaenidae (lion fish). Many of these fish frequent deep habitats, hence they will quickly suffer from too much light.

The marine aquarist has plenty of latitude for experimenting with lighting. Using one Grolux or Magnalux bulb to grow algae and also an assortment of different colored light bulbs will yield odd and sometimes beautiful effects. Anyone ever visiting the Bronx Zoo in New York can see an exhibit devoted to nocturnal animals; this lighting effect should stimulate ideas for displaying many inhabitants of deeper waters. The use of dark red lights will give many fish a more natural effect and, many times in this way, will highlight the display of fish. The New York Aquarium also has an aquarium specially lighted for nocturnal fishes.

TABLE 6

ALGAE FOUND AT DIFFERENT DEPTHS

Type of Algae	Spectrum Absorbed	Depth
Blue green	red and yellow	Shallow
Green	blues and red	No deeper than 20 ft.
Brown	green through blue	Wide range
Red	green and blue	Deeper than 20 ft.

An established marine aquarium with a good growth of green algae. (photo credit: R. Valenti)

Temperature

The optimum temperature at which marine fish and invertebrates are maintained is in the 70-80° F. range. The higher the water temperature the greater the metabolic rate; therefore more waste products excreted by the fish. Keeping this in mind, it is often wiser to keep the fish nearer their lower temperature tolerance level, especially if the tank is crowded with fish or the fish are large. High temperatures will often cause parasites such as <u>Oodinium</u> to bloom in the aquarium. This does not mean, of course, if the temperature is kept at 70° F there will be fewer, if any, parasites; but simply that there will be fewer parasites at 70° F than at 80° F. There are only a few aquarium systems which are capable of cooling sea water. These systems are usually very efficient in supporting invertebrate and vertebrate growth but are also quite expensive. If a specific problem does arise, where the aquarium must be cooled, simply immerse a loop of rubber hose, which is carrying cold water from a faucet, into the aquarium, and then allow it to flow into a sink. This arrangement will lower the water temperature approximately 5°.

THE ESTABLISHED MARINE AQUARIUM

Having discussed the principle of water chemistry, I would like to list the ingredients for a well-balanced marine aquarium:

1. A newly constructed lucite or glass aquarium should be rinsed several times with tap water.

2. Distribute two inches of limestone or calcite chips over a subsand filter which should cover at least 1/3 of the tank bottom.

3. Purchase a substantially powerful outside filter which provides as much surface area as possible.

4. The top of the aquarium should be covered no more than 50%; the return flow from the filter should break the surface of the water.

5. Cultivate a rich growth of algae.

6. Ultra-violet light or ozone gas should be used infrequently, if at all, and only at such times as to decrease excessive bacterial growth causing cloudyness.

7. Control aeration; avoid supersaturation of water with gases.

8. Cautiously maintain temperature at 70-80° F. and also salinity between 30-36°/oo.

9. Maintain pH at 8.0-8.3.

10. The aquarium should be cleaned once every 8 months, when handling a normal capacity of fish and at this time new salt water should be used (allow one week for tank to readjust before adding fish). Cleaning more frequently than every 6 months is unnecessary and can be harmful. Changing 1/4 of the tank water every 2 months can be done if care is taken to add only aged water. The addition of extra trace elements is beneficial but should not be used in place of water changes. Additional trace elements added every 2 or 3 months will replace those elements used by fish and invertebrates. Periodic water changes will remove organic material as well as nitrates which tend to build up in a closed system.

TABLE 7
APPROXIMATE WATER TEMPERATURES AT SURFACE AND 200 METERS

	SURFACE	200 METERS (600 Ft.)
Atlantic Ocean (Florida Coast)	27°C	15-20°C
	80°F	59-68°F
Pacific Coastal Region	20-25°C	9-10°C
	68-77°F	48-50°F
Pacific Ocean (Hawaii)	25°C	15-22°C
	77°F	59-72°F
Indian Ocean	23-25°C	15-20°C
	73-77°F	59-68°F

WATER CHEMISTRY BIBLIOGRAPHY

Atz, J. 1964 Some principles and practices of water management for marine aquariums, pp. 3-16 In: *Sea Water Systems for Experimental Aquariums, J.* Clark and R. Clark (editors), Bureau of Sport Fisheries and Wildlife.

Harvey, H. 1966 *The Chemistry and Fertility of Sea waters,* Cambridge University Press, Great Britain, 240 p.

Herald, E., R. Dempster, C. Walters and M. Hunt. 1962. Filtration and ultraviolet sterilization of sea water in large closed, and semi-closed systems, Communications les Congrés International d'Aquariologie, B., pp. 49-61.

Horne, R.A. 1970 *Marine Chemistry,* Wiley-Interscience, New York, 568 p.

Kelly, W. 1963 Ideal configuration for a semi-closed circulating aquarium system, Program, 50th anniversary meeting, American Society of Ichthyologist and Herpetologist, p. 43, Abstract.

Oliver, J. 1957 The chemical composition of the sea water in the aquarium, Proceeding of the Zoological Society of London, 129 (1), pp. 137-145.

Spotte, S.H. 1970 *Fish and Invertebrate Culture,* John Wiley and Sons, Inc., N.Y. 145 p.

Strickland, J.D.H. and T.R. Parsons 1968 *A Practical Handbook of Seawater Analysis,* Bull. Fish. Res. Bd. Canada, 167:311 p.

Sverdrup, H.U., M. Johnson and R. Flemming. 1942 *The Oceans,* Prentice-Hall, New York, 1087 p.

A calcareous marine algae
(photo credit: R. Valenti)

CHAPTER 3

MARINE PLANTS

Marine plants may be classified as algae possessing holdfasts or rhizoids as opposed to flowering plants which have true roots, leaves, and stems. Some are microscopic in size and are among the smallest plants in existence while others are quite large, for example, kelp, one of the largest plants, can attain a leaf size of 100 feet. Except for some fungi, virtually all marine plants are autophytic, which means they are capable of producing their own food. Self-feeding is accomplished through the process of photosynthesis, in which water, carbon dioxide, and sunlight are used to produce a carbohydrate-food substance. Marine plants are usually not found in deep waters; they are limited to relatively shallow waters and intertidal regions through which sunlight can penetrate. They are classified into three major groups depending upon their pigmentation: the green algae, the brown algae and the red algae.

The discussion of marine algae was briefly mentioned in Chapter 2; this section will stress identification and growth requirements of selected algae which will be suitable for the aquarium.

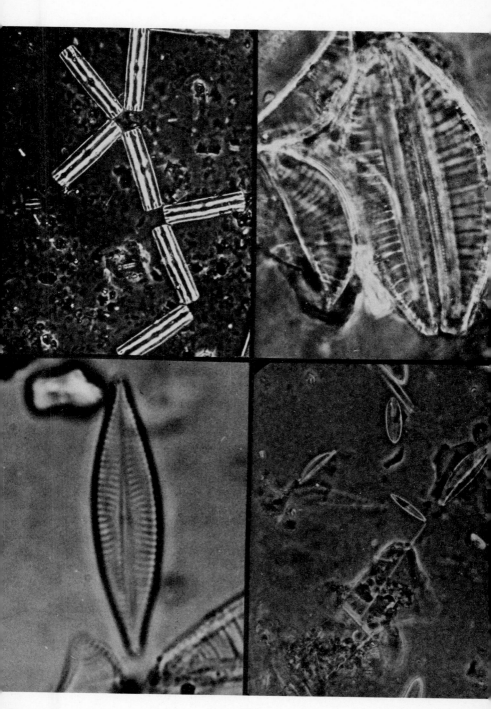

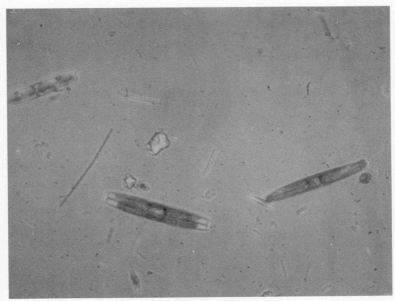

Marine diatoms (photo credit: J.J. Lee)

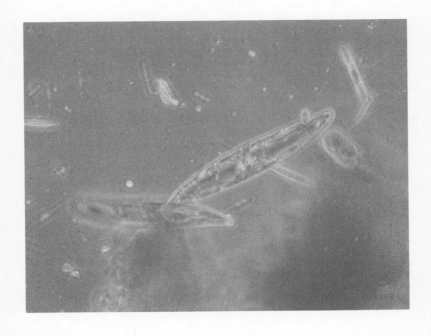

The average marine aquarist will find it difficult to maintain marine plants, but with a certain dedication, it can be a worthwhile venture. In selecting plants which should thrive, consider the following information: plants inhabiting intertidal zones do not thrive well in aquariums since their daily cycle involves desiccation as a result of the tide. Plants which are usually found at depths of 30 feet or more also will not do well in an aquarium (30 feet represents two atmospheres, which means the pressure per square inch of surface area is double that which they will receive in an aquarium).

There are several types of green algae that inhabit shallow water, which do well under artificial conditions. It goes without saying that only healthy specimens, free of damage, should be planted. Care should be taken to cover the rhizoids superficially. After transferring a plant, at least twenty-four hours of constant lighting should be provided to stimulate and encourage food production; thereafter, a daily exposure to 6-8 hours of incandescent lighting is sufficient. The use of aquarium plant foods containing nutritive nitrates and phosphates will greatly enhance marine plant growth.

The aquarist should be aware that omnivorous fish and invertebrates are also herbivorous. Occasionally then, the submarine meadows of the tank will be harvested as their dietary supplement. This situation can be annoying and also detrimental to the aquarium's stability and beauty. If the plant growth rate is low and the appetites of the herbivores ravenous, complete elimination of the plant life will ensue. To provide a practical change of diet for the plant eaters, portions of Ulva (sea lettuce), either fresh or frozen, can be used.

The plants which belong to the Class Chlorophycea, Order Siphonales, will adapt well to the aquarium. All species are calcified and are found in tropical waters, the temperature of which is approximately 75° F. The utmost care should be exercised to maintain a pH level of 8.0-8.3; acidic water will decalcify these plants and thereby weaken them structurally and biologically. For those species encrusted with carbonate lime, the use of limestone chips will supply abundant amounts of structurally necessary material. The reproduction of these algae is intricate; many times it involves sexual reproduction and the subsequent production of flagellated gametes. Botanists, for example, once thought that the obvious structures on Udotea fabellum were reproductive, however, they were merely encrusted symbiotic animals.

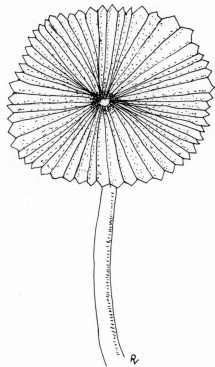

Diagram III

Acetabularia crenulata, Sea pansy

<u>Acetabularia crenulata,</u> (Sea Pansy)

                Class   Chlorophyceae
                Order   Siphonales
                Family Dasycladaceae

    This highly attractive, one inch sized, single-celled algae grows on corals, rocks and many other objects. Though a rusty can is not very attractive and not likely to be found in a home aquarium, <u>Acetabularia</u> often decorates these in nature. <u>Acetabularia</u> is difficult to maintain in the tank as it demands a great deal of light. It is usually encrusted with carbonate of lime and therefore, needs alkaline conditions. Interestingly, if the whorl of the leaf-like filaments on the anterior end breaks, a new whorl will be formed. This occurs since the nucleus of this single-celled plant is found in the holdfast and the extra amount of cytoplasm which is represented by the whorl is not essential for survival. Often some species of this plant will have two sets of whorls, one will be fertile and the other sterile.

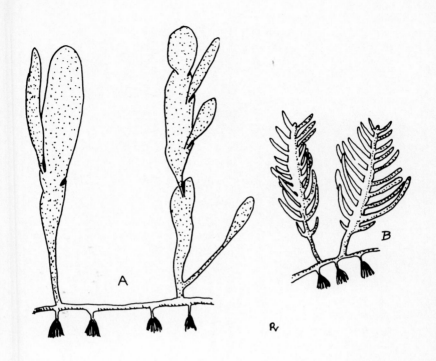

Diagram IV

A. *Caulerpa prolifera,* sea pen
B. *C. crassifolia,* sea pen

Caulerpa prolifera, (Sea Pen)
　　　　　　　　Class　　Chlorophyceae
　　　　　　　　Order　　Siphonales
　　　　　　　　Family　Caulerpaceae

　　Caulerpa prolifera, C. crassifolia, C. sertulanoides, C. ashmeadii and
C. paspaloides all do especially well in the marine aquarium. These
plants have a creeping stolon with numerous sand penetrating rhizoids.
From the creeping rhizome, numerous plants will develop and the
aquarium can easily take on the appearance of a small forest. Caulerpa
is a green algae with broad leaves and for this reason are capable
of persisting under dimly lighted conditions. Some of these species are
found at depths of 15 to 50 meters or more. A great number of these
species adhere to rocks and corals. The shapes of these plants vary from
specie to specie but their maximum height of approximately 12
inches is fairly consistent.

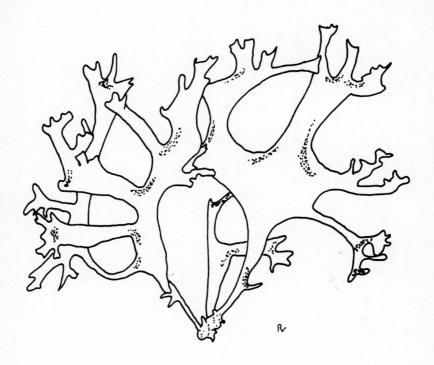

Diagram V

Chondrus crispus, Irish moss

Chondrus crispus,   (Irish Moss)
                        Class   Rhodophyceae
                        Order   Gigartinales
                        Family   Gigartinaceae

Chondrus crispus, a red algae commonly called Irish moss, is found on the North Eastern coast of the United States, in intertidal regions and at moderate depths. It can be kept in an aquarium if the temperature of the water is 55-60° F, but at warmer temperatures it will not survive. This plant needs a limited amount of light, only 4-6 hours daily, and although it is usually a reddish color, it will turn green with strong illumination. Healthy specimens are fan shaped with irregularly patterned leaves and reach a size of approximately 8 inches.

43

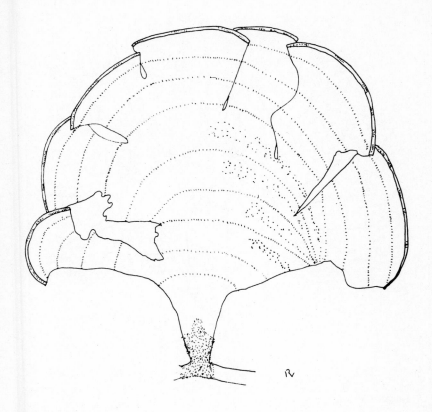

Diagram VI

Padina vickersiae, ruffled sea fan

Padina vickersiae, (Ruffled Seafan)
                   Class   Phaeophyceae
                   Order   Dictyotales
                   Family   Dictyotaceae

This very delicate brown algae has several irregularly shaped blades. The edges of the blades are raveled and tiny hair-like structures are distributed on the surface of the plant. P. vickersiae is highly calcareous, has a rigid appearance, and is tan colored. This plant has a wide geographic range and is found in warm, shallow seas. P. vickersiae is found growing in rock pools, which are small pockets of water remaining after the tide goes out. Most specimens remain small and seldom exceed 3 or 4 inches.

Diagram VII

Penicillus capitatus, Neptune's shaving brush

Penicillus capitatus, (Neptune's Shaving Brush)
                    Class   Chlorophyceae
                    Order   Siphonales
                    Family   Codiaceae

    This oddly shaped plant well deserves its nickname, Neptune's Shaving Brush. The plant has a terminal tuft of filaments which gives this calcified algae its name. Penicillus is usually found anchored in sandy and muddy bottoms of warm, non-turbulent waters. Under natural conditions, this green plant often forms large meadows of growth which provide excellent feeding and spawning grounds for fish and invertebrates. Care should be taken that these plants are in good condition before purchasing them. If grown properly, they will retain their pale green color and will be quite firm in texture. Aquarium specimens are usually 3-5 inches in height.

Diagram VIII

Rhipocephalus phoenix, sea cone

Rhipocephalus phoenix,   (Sea Cone)
       Class Chlorophyceae
       Order Siphonales
       Family Codiaceae
  This plant resembles Penicillus, though, instead of a terminal tuft of free filaments, small, narrow fan shaped leaves are stacked in layers. Older specimens bear an astonishing resemblance to Penicillus in that the fan shapped leaves become filamentous. Rhipocephalus can be maintained easily by providing a fine sand substrate, a water temperature of 75-80° F, and six to eight hours of lighting. A good method for growing these plants under aquarium conditions is to plant them in a flat plastic container with humus soil which is then covered by sand or limestone. This method is an excellent one for growing any of the marine plants that are difficult to maintain. An alkaline medium should be provided since this plant does become encrusted with calcium carbonate.

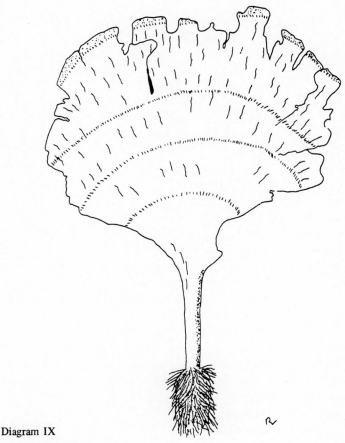

Diagram IX

Udotea flabellum, sea fan

Udotea flabellum,   (Sea Fan)
                       Class   Chlorophyceae
                       Order   Siphonales
                       Family Codiaceae

    Udotea flabellum is a fan shaped plant which thrives in aquariums when it is in its juvenile stages, at which time it is three or four inches in size. Looking closely at the fan, the concentric lines represent annual growth. They possess unicellular rhizoids and do well planted in fine sand and exposed to six hours of light. This plant is often found in warm waters and encrusted with carbonate of lime. Some members characteristically deposit calcium carbonate around their filaments and are the largest and most conspicuous of the calcareous green algae.

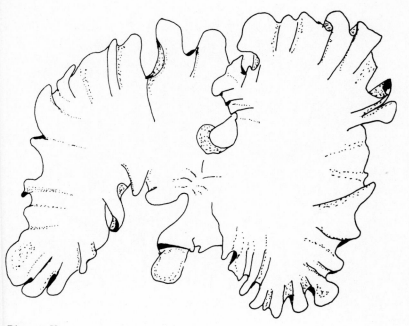

Diagram X

Ulva, Sea lettuce

R

Ulva spp., (Sea Lettuce)
    Class   Chlorophyceae
    Order   Ulotrichales
    Family   Ulotrichaceae
    These plants have a widespread geographic distribution, being found both in the warm waters of Bermuda and Florida and in the cold waters of Newfoundland and the Hudson Bay. It is easily collected along the sea shore but care should be taken to collect plants of bright green color and possessing a holdfast. Many fragments of this plant, known commonly as sea lettuce, are found strewn about beaches due to a turbulent surf. Success of raising this plant in the marine aquarium depends on duplicating the temperature requirements. Those plants collected in warm water areas will do nicely if given 6 hours of incandescent light and a water temperature of 70-75° F. Plants collected in cooler waters must be provided with water temperatures of 55-60° F., which is difficult to provide without a cooling system. It is not necessary to plant the holdfast below the gravel if it is already attached to a stone, as it usually is.

Sargassum weed often found floating freely in
the Gulf Stream. (photo credit: R. Valenti)

Cymopolia barbata, a common plant of shallow water areas
of Southern Florida, (photo credit: R. Valenti)

MARINE ALGAE
BIBLIOGRAPHY

Dawson, Yale E. 1956. *How to Know the Seaweeds*. Wm. C. Brown Co., Dubuque, Iowa. 197 pp.

Dawson, Yale E. 1966. *Marine Botany*. Holt, Rinehart and Winston, Inc., New York, 377 pp.

Fritsch, F. E. 1965. *The Structures and Reproduction of the Algae.* Vol. I and II, Cambridge University Press, Great Britain.

Segawa, S. 1968. *Colored Illustrations of the Sea Weeds of Japan*, Hoikusha Pub. Co., Japan, 175 p.

Taylor, W. R. 1960. *Marine Algae of the Eastern Tropical and Subtropical Coasts of America.* The University of Michigan Press, Ann Arbor, Michigan. 882 pp.

Taylor, W.R. 1962. *Marine Algae of the Northeastern Coast of North America.* The University of Michigan Press, Ann Arbor, Michigan. 509 pp.

CHAPTER 4

MARINE INVERTEBRATES

Invertebrates may be defined simply as cold blooded organisms without any vertebrae. Marine aquariums usually display an abundance of fish and, if any, one or two invertebrates. This situation is quite the opposite to that which occurs in the sea where the invertebrates represent the major percentage of the marine population. The invertebrates are less popular in the aquarium since they are difficult to maintain. The problem in maintaining these animals stems from their diverse nutritional requirements and habitats.

Invertebrates, such as clams and mussels, don't often thrive in captivity since temperature and nutritional demands cannot be fulfilled adequately. These creatures feed by means of adapted structures through which they filter many gallons of sea water each day; since there is not an abundant supply of microscopic food organisms in a closed aquarium, they quickly perish. Although many filtering invertebrates do best in an aquarium with natural sea water, synthetic salts can also be used with success if the necessary food organisms are introduced regularly. Intertidal animals, such as barnacles, can be nutritionally satisfied; however, since they require daily desiccation it becomes inopportune to create a mechanical tidal system to satisfy this need. This deficiency seems to block their survival in the marine aquarium.

There are several groups of invertebrates which will manage quite nicely in the aquarium; some will even contribute to its chemical stability. Scavengers, such as some crabs, shrimp, lobsters, feather duster worms, snails, corals, and sea anemones, will constantly degrade and filter the detritus.

These diverse and interesting creatures will be high lighted in this chapter and special attention will be drawn to those invertebrates which can be easily maintained and which will contribute to the uniqueness of the marine aquarium.

PROTOZOA

This highly diverse group of single-celled animals are of small or microscopic size, but are a significant link in the food chain. Some are motile due to the presence of cilia and flagella; others are sessile and are attached to the substrate by a disc or stalk. Some members of the population are pigmented (red, brown, orange and green). The green animals contain chlorophyll, which is very important in the photosynthetic process. Some protozoans are naked and others are

Marine tunicates, *Distaplia occidentalis,*
a representative of the phylum Chordata.
(photo credit: Ward's Natural Science
establishment)

protected by spines of silica and strontium (See Radiolarian, on cover). Others secrete a cement that eventually becomes studded with sand grains and even colorful chips of glass.

In general, the aquarist should become acquainted with protozoa since they form an abundant part of the marine biota, and some, no doubt, constitute a major source of food for young fish. An initial problem in raising marine fishes from the larval stage is a lack of available food that is small enough to be eaten and digested; these microscopic organisms fit this niche quite naturally. Marine ciliated protozoa, for example, can be cultured as easily as fresh water ciliates and fed in abundance to larval fish. Other important protozoans, that are parasitic, i.e., dinoflagellates and sporozoans, will be discussed in Chapter 6. It is not in the realm of this book to discuss the adventures and attributes of these fascinating creatures but the interested aquarist is referred to the bibliography for more extensive readings.

PORIFERA (sponges)

Sponges are one of the most primitive groups of multicellular animals. Some of these are sessile and others colonial; some are bright reds and oranges, but most are of drab coloration. They range in size from a pinhead to 8 feet in diameter. Generally, their shape is asymmetrical but this often changes with variations in the environment, for example, in surf areas, where the water is shallow and more turbulent, the sponge will be firm and fan-shaped; if the sponges are in

Typical Marine Sponge
(photo credit:
Douglas Faulkner)

deep water, they will be tall and stately; if they are in barrier pools, the sponges will have more detail as the sea is generally calm in these areas. Most of the sponges are marine with the exception of one fresh water group. There are approximately 5000 species of sponges, some of which can be maintained in a synthetic environment. If living sponges are placed in the aquarium, they should be cleaned well, being rinsed several times in clean sea water. Their arrangement in the aquarium should provide ample room for growth. Optimum growth can be achieved by supplying a quantity of natural sea water at least once a month; one or two gallons will provide the necessary microscopic food particles that are the mainstay of the sponges. A fascinating experiment that questions whether the sponge is an independent individual or merely a composite of efficient single units is to squeeze a small sponge through a piece of cheese cloth. This will cause the disintegration of the sponge into single cells or groups of cells. In an hour or two, separate sponges will be formed from the remnants of the total sponge; this illustrates the capability of the individual cells to organize and survive and the inability of the primitive sponge to completely control or direct its individuality. As part of its reproductive cycle, a ciliated larva is produced which swims about and eventually becomes a sessile structure. The sponges are divided into three groups, the criterion being the type of spicules in each sponge. These spicules are analogous to a primitive skeletal system which provides support for the animal. The spicules can be calcareous, silicious, or fibrous spongin.

1. Calcarea. These are the calcareous sponges which have spicules of calcium carbonate. Many of these are drab in appearance, and smaller than other sponges. This type of sponge is often found in shallow coastal regions.

2. Hexactinellida. These are the sponges whose spicules are composed of silica and are six-sided. They are usually found solitary in nature, and many are beautifully vase or cup shaped, for example, Venus's flower-basket (Euplectella). Unfortunately, these sponges are deep water sponges, 1500 feet to 3 miles down, and if transferred to shallow waters, they do poorly. The Venus's flower-basket engages in a semi-parasitic relationship, called commensalism, with certain shrimp. The young male and female shrimp enter the sponge's cavity and after they reach maturity, are unable to escape but they continue to survive by feeding on the plankton that circulates through the cavity.

3. Demospongia. In this group are the sponges that have silica spicules (not six-sided) and also spongin spicules. The bath sponges belong to this group.

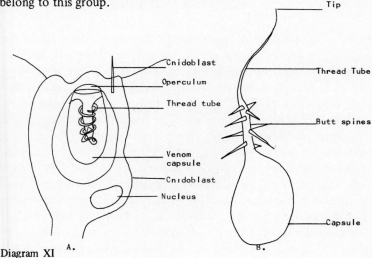

Diagram XI   A.

A. Undischarged nematocyst
B. Discharged nematocyst (based on R. Kreuzinger)

54

Coral polyp—from Bahamas, showing mouth opening
(photo credit: Douglas Faulkner)

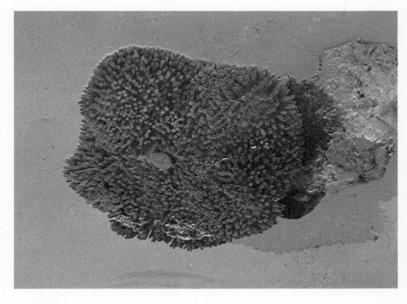

Anemone
(photo credit: R. Valenti)

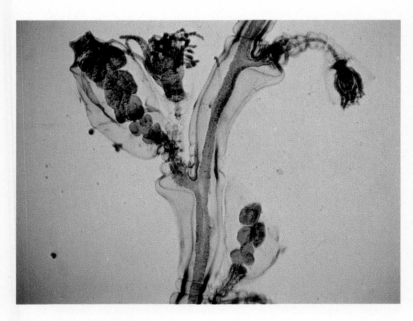

Obelia—detail of hydranth
(photo credit: Ward's Natural Science Establishment)

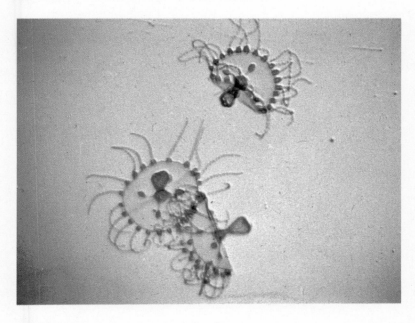

Obelia-medusa
(photo credit: Ward's Natural Science Establishment)

Cassiopia, upside-down jelly fish
(photo credit: H. Freudenthal)

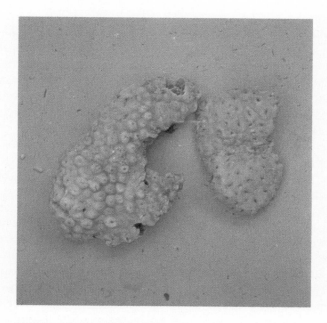

Living coral, removed from the water
(photo credit: R. Valenti)

COELENTERATES

This group comprises approximately 10,000 aquatic species. Most are marine, and all are radially symmetrical. The members of this phylum have one of two shapes; a polyp stage, that is no larger than a few inches and a medusa stage that ranges from 2.3 mm to 12 feet in diameter with tentacles 120 feet long. (Some of these are the largest animals on the face of the earth today). From one generation to the next, these animals may change their shape from polyp- medusa- polyp- medusa, etc.; this is called metagenesis. The separation of these animals into classes depends on their shape and the presence of metagenesis.

Class Hydrozoans: ex. Portugese Man-of-War. Some of these are fresh water inhabitants; others are marine. They typically alternate shape from generation to generation, but the polyp is the prominent stage.

Class Scyphozoans: ex. common jellyfish. These are only marine species, with the dominant stage being the medusae. Metagenesis is characteristic of this class.

Class Anthozoans: ex. sea anemone and coral. Anthozoans, flower animals, are deadly animal traps. There are approximately 6000 species and only polyps are the existing shape.

Hydrozoa

Physalia, the Portugese Man-of-War, is a colonial animal. On the surface of the water is a pinkish gas-filled float, under the float are several different types of polyps (which look like tentacles) each having different shapes and functions. The different types of tentacles show the high degree of variation in a single colony. The Portugese Man-of-War is seldom kept in a marine aquarium due to the length of the tentacles. Stings from these animals can be highly painful.

Scyphozoa

The jellyfish is familiar to many of us but they are usually impossible to maintain in aquariums for long periods of time. If a constant flow of natural sea water is provided the percentage of survival would increase. One of the few jellyfish whose demands can be met in captivity is Cassiopeia, the "upside-down" jellyfish. This species is commonly found in the shallow waters off the Florida coast. This interesting animal lays on the ocean bottom with its stretched tentacles waving above. Cassiopeia has symbiotic algae which grow intracellularly; these yellow brown algae are called zooxanthellae. Both the algae and the jellyfish derive simultaneous nutritional value from this close relationship.

Anthozoa

Sea anemones vary greatly in size, color, and shape but all are attached to the substrate, be it rock, shell, or sand, by a pedal disc.

The anemones are sessile polyps but they can move a limited distance by the following methods: gliding, somersaulting or forming an air bubble under the disc; the bubble breaks and then the polyp moves.

The anemones are gourmets, in that they consider other invertebrates and vertebrates as tasty morsels. Some prefer scallops, brine strimps and some even trap fish. Anemones, though sessile and plant-like, can be deadly to other marine inhabitants. The tentacles of many anemones contain stinging cells or nematocysts which carry a toxin capable of paralyzing prey. Once paralyzed, the prey is immobilized and the anemone's tentacles fold inwardly stuffing the captured victim into its mouth. Often anemones will form a symbiotic relationship with shrimp, crabs and even fish. In the first case, the shrimp live among the tentacles of certain anemones. The shrimp, in turn, attract pedators which are attracted to the idea of a shrimp dinner, but alas, they are the dinner. The once predator, now prey, is paralyzed by the tentacles of the anemones and now both the shrimp and the anemone share the paralyzed victim. Many of the clown fish, Amphiprion, are found to inhabit large anemones in a symbiotic relationship. Fishelson, in his work on Red Sea anemones, points out that there are non-symbiotic and symbiotic anemones of which only the latter are inhabited by Amphiprion. Fishelson also indicates that the clown fish are necessary to the health of the anemone in that they remove the mucus coating which is continually formed by the anemone. The fish were also found to drop morsels of food into the mouth of the anemone. In return the fish are guaranteed a place of protection against predators and the base of the anemone also provides a spawning site and a place near which to deposit eggs. Crabs are often seen with anemones atop their shells and they use them as weapons with which to paralyze prey, and then again both can share a dinner. The aquarist should, of course, avoid placing any burrowing fish such as wrasses into an aquarium containing anemones since they may emerge from the sand under the anemone and swim, inadvertently, into the deadly tentacles. Many of the smaller anemones are quite suitable for the marine aquarium and will do little to harm the fish.

The sea anemones reproduce by splitting longitudinally, or forming buds off the parent, or by piederlasceration, which means if as much as .0006 inch of an anemone is cut from the disc, this piece will grow into an individual anemone. Piederlasceration usually occurs when the animal glides.

Sea anemones, like the jellyfish, have symbiotic algae. The green algae use the carbon dioxide, that is released as a by-product of the sea anemone's metabolism, in photosynthesis. It is believed that the carbohydrate produced in photosynthesis is used as a food substance by the anemone. Here again is an example of the inter-dependence of marine life. When the anemones are placed in the aquarium, six hours of daily light should supply the necessary stimulus for the photosynthesis of the algae.

The aquarist should be aware of these two factors when purchasing anemones:

1. If the stomach is everted through the mouth, this is usually a sign of illness in many invertebrates.

2. Be concerned that the pedal disc is not ripped or bruised. This can often occur during collecting.

The living coral is a small anemone-like polyp, with short tentacles, no pedal disc, and lives in a stony cup with a radially banded bottom. They require a water temperature of $70°$ F. or warmer and they live near the surface to depths of 120 feet. They, too, have symbiotic algae, zooxanthellae.

Studies done on the rates of calcium deposition by corals shows that corals deposit ten times as much calcium in the light as in the dark and that those corals having no algae show a uniformly low rate of calcium deposition. This decrease or increase of calcium deposition is explained by two theories:

1. Oxygen liberated from the zooxanthellae in the photosynthetic process is made available to the polyp of living coral. The oxygen, in turn, triggers the metabolic activity of the corals. With the more rapid metabolic rate there is a coincidental increase in the layers of calcium deposition, which is deposited as calcium carbonate.

2. The carbon dioxide released by the polyp in metabolism is used by the zooxanthellae in photosynthesis to form a carbohydrate food substance.

This relationship is similar to that in which the anemones are involved. If the anemone or coral polyp is not given an ample supply of light, it will shrink in size due to the retarded rate of photosynthesis. It is, therefore, important to supply corals, and sea anemones with a strong source of light; at least six hours each day. This light is best supplied by aiming an incandescent bulb near the organisms but avoiding any unnecessary heat.

Madreporian corals, although again closely related to the sea anemones, produce a calcium carbonate skeleton. This skeleton is secreted by the coral polyp which is within a cup-like depression. The polyps of corals are all interconnected by a sheet of calcium. The coral polyps feed in a similar way to anemones except feeding is in the evening. Crustaceans such as newly hatched brine shrimp are devoured by the ciliary action of the tentacles. There are, of course, many different skeletal configurations of coral depending on the particular species. The size of the coral is also very diverse but if one keeps in mind that some large corals can add one inch of growth every hundred days, it is easy to understand how an entire coral island or reef can be formed. Those corals which are most desirable for the aquarium are found in shallow areas where a great deal of light is available. While some publications have suggested the use of strong aeration for growth of corals, I would certainly avoid this. Corals, like many marine fish and invertebrates, will produce waste products in the form of ammonia which will be broken down to nitrogen with the help of algae. Excessive aeration with atmospheric gases will only increase the nitrogen content of the water. In maintaining coral it is important to keep the pH at 8.0-8.3. The presence of calcium carbonate is, of course, essential but this is already present in an abundant amount in either synthetic or natural salts. If several large pieces of coral are being kept in a closed system with adequate filtration, it is advisable to change ¼ of the water monthly to replace the depleted mineral salts, which were utilized by the corals.

Alcyonarian corals, include those corals such as sea pens, sea fans, and pipe corals. These corals possess smaller polyps than do the stony or Madreporian corals. A major difference is that the Alcyonarian corals possess an internal skeleton which is covered by tissue as opposed to the stony corals which have an external skeleton. In general, the sea fans, Gorgonia, are perhaps the most commonly kept of these corals and seem to thrive well in the aquarium if it is balanced chemically and physically. It is important to remember that most invertebrates are highly sensitive to changes in salinity, temperature, and pH. Sudden variations should be avoided.

The October 1966 Scientific American discussed the evidence that the bands or layers of calcium deposition, on certain corals represented annual, monthly and daily growth. Ancient corals therefore provide a contemporary clue to the length of the year in past eras and to the changes in the rotations of the earth. These corals are "PALEONTOLOGICAL CLOCKS" to astronomers, geophysicists and other investigators who wish to reliably measure the age of the earth.

Spirobranchus sp., tube worms protruding out of a
piece of coral.
(photo credit: Marine Tropical Imports, Inc.)

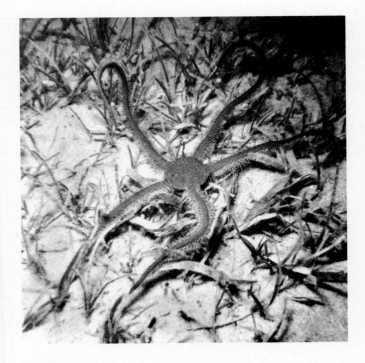

Brittle starfish
(photo credit: Douglas Faulkner)

ANNELIDS

Annelids are mostly marine, segmented, round worms, with a world-wide distribution. They may be microscopic or range up to 9 feet long (one inch in diameter). The classification depends on whether they are errant or sedentary. This phylum contains the beautiful fan worms. These creatures form sand granule tubes or tubes from the calcium carbonate in the water, which protect their soft bodies. They are often found at the base of a piece of coral where they will periodically expand their tentacles to collect particles of food. These tentacles are also the means by which an exchange of gases takes place. They survive by eating newly hatched brine shrimp, grated beef hearts, or pieces of scallop. At times, large organisms resembling oversized tubeworms (3-4 inches long) are purchased but these are coelenterates. These coelenterates often burrow in the sand but never near an undergravel filter, since the circulation of water through the sand is undesirable for them.

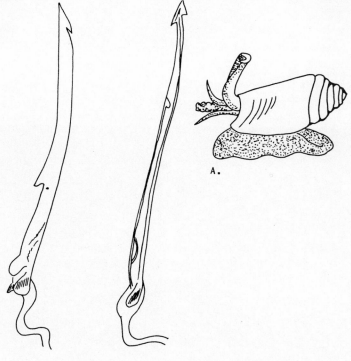

Diagram XII

A. External features of typical cone shell.
B. Radula teeth of two representative species of venomous cone shells.
   Conus marmoreus X 200 (left), and *Conus tulipa* X 140 (right)

63

Conus marmoreus, can be toxic
(photo credit: Douglas Faulkner)

Sabellid tube worms are an attractive sight in an
aquarium and are "biological" filters.
(photo credit: Marine Tropical Imports, Inc.)

A sea hare, which is an apisthobranch. Note the rhinophores at the anterior end used as chemoreceptors. (photo credit: Marine Tropical Imports, Inc.)

MOLLUSKS

This phylum is represented by such familiar forms as the clam, oyster, squid, and snail. Most of these animals can survive in a marine aquarium. The mollusks are soft bodied animals usually having protective shells. This phylum has approximately 80,000 species and for this reason is the second largest invertebrate group; of these, 35,000 are known fossil species. They have varied habitats and requirements; some are land creatures; some are aquatic, either fresh or salt; some are filter feeders and others are parasitic. They range in size from 1/2 inch to the giant clam which may weigh 25 pounds (excluding the shell). The blood of many invertebrates contains copper as a respiratory pigment. The copper content of their blood makes them more sensitive to additional amounts of copper in the aquarium.

Class Pelecypoda

Clams, mussels and scallops, if kept, should be confined to the filter box since they need a tremendous amount of organic debris. Actually a filter box is an ideal place for these animals since they constantly filter water through their siphons. The aquarist should be extremely careful with these organisms because if they are not fed enough and subsequently die, in a matter of hours decay will start and bacteria will bloom. Locomotion in the clam is by means of their muscular foot which becomes rigid through engorgement with blood.

Often small scallops, which have a certain beauty, are welcome aquarium members. They seem to survive better than clams or mussels. Scallops also exhibit fascinating behavioral mechanisms; their rapid movement permits them to avoid their natural enemy, the starfish. As an aid to movement they use a well developed muscle to open and close their hinged shells. Locomotion is accomplished by the synchronous squirting out of water between the shells as they close.

Class Amphineura

One of the most primitive mollusks is the chiton which has an elliptically shaped body bearing eight overlapping jointed plates. It is a handsome and hardy addition to an aquarium. They range in size from ½ inch to over a foot. They seldom locomote but attach tightly to rocks by means of their powerful, muscular foot. They are herbivorous and therefore munch algae from rocks and shells.

Class Gastropoda

The Gastropods are successful inhabitants of the marine aquarium, even where other invertebrates fail. Marine snails, like the fresh water variety, are highly efficient scavengers. They will often burrow in the sand until a piece of food is deposited in the aquarium, at which time they quickly become active and search for a tiny morsel. They do not exhibit any dietary preferences and they can thrive for months without food, even a small piece of algae will satiate them. Snails, however, do present a threat since they secrete a slime upon which they glide. It suffices to say that a larger snail will become increasingly troublesome by producing larger quantities of slime which can cause bacteria to grow. Several of the brightly colored cone snails are predators and are responsible for paralyzing and eating some fish. These snails capture their prey by spearing them with their radula tooth, a rasping device, which is characteristic of most mollusks (except clams). Fortunately the cannibalistic genus Conus, are rarely found in aquariums. The radula, depending on the genus of gastropods, may serve different purposes. Some are used for tearing holes in plants and cutting pieces of food material, while others have become adapted to drill holes in the calcium shells of other invertebrates.

Sea slugs, or nudibranchs, do not have a shell as do the other gastropods. They are the most beautiful of all the mollusks, as many are brilliantly colored red, orange, yellow, green, and blue. Most lack gills and respiration occurs through the body surface and is facilitated by numerous projections or cerata found on the dorsal surface. Most of the nudibranches are small, one to two inches in size, and can be easily

66

maintained in the aquarium. They prefer temperatures of 75-80° F; although there are a few cold water species, 50-60° F. Nudibranchs should not be included in the same tank with anemones. The nudibranchs are not deterred by the anemone's stinging cells or nematocysts. Frequently the nudibranchs incorporate these defensive cells into their own cell structure. The nematocysts are then fully controlled and are completely functional in their new host. Occasionally, the aquarist can remove an anemone's tentacle and hand-feed it to the nudibranch. It, in turn, will devour the fragment and the anemone will be none the worse since their tentacles have a high regenerative capacity. Sea slugs, should also be fed bits of clam and scallop and occasionally pieces of Ulva or other vegetation.

Class Cephalopoda

Squids, while highly interesting, are extremely difficult to maintain in an aquarium and they should be avoided since they release toxic substances which are lethal to other tank inhabitants. Octopods, while also capable of secreting toxic substances, can be kept as the sole inhabitant of an aquarium if an efficient filtration system is available. There have been several instances where octopods have been reported to lay their eggs while in an aquarium situation.

Sea anemones, *Calliactis* sp., festoon the shell of a hermit crab, *Dardanus venosus.* The anemones eat organic material stirred up by the crab and in turn provide protection for the crab. (photo credit: Marine Tropical Imports, Inc.)

Small hermit crabs are excellent scavengers for the marine aquarium.
This one has taken up occupancy in a *Conus* sp. shell.
(photo credit: Marine Tropical Imports, Inc.)

Stenopus hispidus, banded coral shrimp
(photo credit: Douglas Faulkner)

Paraclimentes yucatanicus, cleaner
shrimp on sea anemone, *Condylactis gigantea*
(photo credit: Douglas Faulkner)

Hymenocera elegans, elegant
coral shrimp
(photo credit: Douglas Faulkner)

Spiny lobster
(photo credit: John G. Shedd Aquarium)

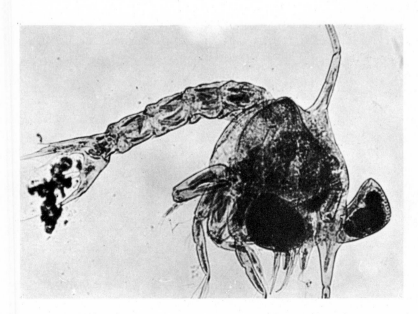

Zoea, larval crab
(photo credit: R. Valenti)

Nauplius larvae of brine shrimp
(photo credit: R. Valenti)

ARTHROPODS

This phylum is by far the largest and most anatomically diverse. There are more than 800,000 species. This number represents 80% of all known animal species. Most arthropods have three distinguishable body regions: head, thorax, and abdomen. Some have light sensitve organs for seeing; others have more highly developed compound eyes; tactile hairs and antennae are touch sensitive; small palps increase the sensitivity to chemical changes, and auditory hairs facilitate hearing. Besides these sense organs, arthropods are covered by an organic external skeleton which contains chitin. This skeleton not only affords protection to the animal but also provides a structure to which muscles can attach. Paired appendages are used for swimming, crawling, cleaning the body, defense, offense, and feeding. Some arthropods have gills which are found internally in the thorasic region; and others are external: book gills, such as those found in the horseshoe crab. The gills function in the exchange of gases, i.e., release of carbon dioxide and uptake of oxygen.

Although there are five classes of arthropods only crustaceans inhabit the marine environment (with the exception of a few Arachnids).

Class Crustacea

Copepods are small, microscopic, crustaceans ranging in size from 1-3 millimeters in length. There are some parasitic copepods which are larger. Pennella, a parasitic copepod of fish and whales, often reaches a length of a foot or more (see Chapter 6). The importance of copepods, to the aquarist, is merely the nutritional value they can provide. Copepods comprise the bulk of the zooplankton in the ocean and contribute an important role in the food chain. It is the zooplankton that forms the basic food component of many fish and invertebrates. While it is difficult to culture most copepods in large quantities as food for other organisms, it is now possible to purchase a particular species, Calanus finmarchicus. This fish food, sold as a paste, makes up a major percentage of plankton. The aquarist, who would like to collect living copepods, needs only a single piece of equipment; a plankton net. Plankton nets are fine mesh nets capable of filtering particles from the water. A homemade net, made of a nylon stocking, kept open at one end by a wire ring, is quite functional. By tying a rope to a boat and towing, plankton will collect in the net. The amount of plankton obtained will be roughly proportional to the amount of water that has flowed through the net. Remember, if the net is very fine and dragged at fast speeds, only a very small volume of water will pass through the net. Knowing where to look for plankton is difficult since they aggregate randomly throughout the surface and deeper regions of the seas.

The subclass Cirripedia includes the barnacle. All adult members of this subclass are sessile, some are attached, others are parasitic. Louis Agassiz described a barnacle as "...nothing more than a little shrimp-like animal, standing on its head in a limestone house and kicking the food into its mouth". Barnacles may be divided into stalked and nonstalked types. The stalked type attach to the substrate by means of a peduncle, with the main body or capitulum at the other pole. The nonstalked or sessile barnacles attach by "cementing" themselves to an object. Most barnacles feed on the plankton which adheres to a fan shaped structure of cirri. It is then quickly withdrawn, carrying food to the mouth. Although barnacles can be kept in marine aquaria with some success, they are difficult to maintain for a long time. Most barnacles, even if fed properly, will not survive for more than two or three months. This may be due to the lack of desiccation. There are several barnacles which are commensal or parasitic on a variety of other animals. Crabs are often found carrying one or two barnacles on their carapaces.

The mantis shrimp, Subclass Malacostraca, range in size from 1½ inches to one foot in length. Most are from tropical waters and are brilliantly colored blue, red, and green. They live in burrows which they excavate in the sand beneath pieces of coral by rapidly beating their tails. Unfortunately, for the aquarist, these shrimp feed upon fish and other invertebrates, so it is not wise to keep large specimens in a tank containing smaller organisms. Care should be taken to avoid touching their large, sharp thorasic appendages.

Starfish, from New Caledonia
(photo credit: Douglas Faulkner)

Deep sea starfish from Hawaii
(photo credit: Douglas Faulkner)

73

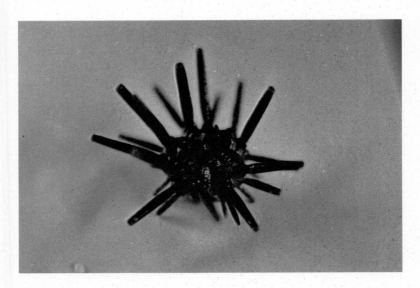

Pencil urchin
(photo credit: R. Valenti)

Feather worm
(photo credit: Douglas Faulkner)

ECHINODERMS

These organisms are exclusively marine, nonparasitic and are usually bottom dwellers. Characteristic of this group is their radial symmetry, that is, the body can be divided into equal parts arranged around a central axis. They all have an internal skeleton composed of calcareous plates. The spiny projections or tubercules so typical on the surface of echinoderms give the body surface a warty appearance, hence the name echinoderm (spiny skin). Echinoderms have a peculiar system of canals comprising the water vascular system. This is the system by which the echinoderm are capable of creating suction. The tube feet create a negative pressure mechanism and are thereby capable of locomotion. The class Stelleroidea contains all starfish or sea stars. Although most starfish possess 5 arms there are a few species which possess as many as 20. The starfish will do nicely in the aquarium provided they are well fed. In those starfish with short, slightly inflexible arms, the prey, be it clam, mussel or scallop, is swallowed whole, digested and the shell is eliminated later. Those having long flexible arms evert their stomachs out their mouth and engulf their prey. The digestive process, therefore, begins outside the body and when the food is reduced to a semi-liquid, it is passed into the body. It is advisable to select small specimens as feeding will be easier. Interestingly, starfish can regenerate their arms; in fact, an arm with one-fifth of the central disc attached can regenerate the rest of the body.

The class Echinoidea comprises the sand dollars and sea urchins each of which are very popular in marine aquariums. Urchins, like starfish, come in a variety of different species, sizes and colors. They are quite interesting to watch and can also be beneficial since they are extremely sensitive to water conditions. Many public aquariums use sea urchins to determine if the water is safe for fish. The aquarist may find this technique useful in testing water quality. If the salt water is not at the proper pH, salinity or temperature, they will begin to drop their spines. Sea urchins feed on all types of organic material, living or dead. As with clams and mussels, these animals seem content when placed into a filter containing a quantity of bottom ooze. If the urchin is turned over, a view of its beak-like mouth apparatus called Aristotle's lantern can be seen. Since urchins derive nutritional benefits from particles in the sand, it is a good idea to provide them with a debris laden area in the aquarium. This area should not be covered by an undergravel filter; of course, if algal mats are growing on the bottom, there is no need to delete the undergravel filter.

The basket starfish, which is an interestingly shaped animal has not been known to survive under aquarium conditions. Often these animals will break apart in the shipping process and only fragments will remain.

The class Holothurians includes the sea cucumbers. These organisms should not be placed in a community aquarium since several species are capable of secreting a highly toxic substance which quickly kills the other inhabitants, both fish and invertebrates alike. In this manner, the sea cucumber has no competition in his environment. While some of the sea cucumbers do not secrete any toxin, they are often difficult to feed since they are filter feeders.

INVERTEBRATES
BIBLIOGRAPHY

Barnes, R. 1966. *Invertebrate Zoology.* W.B. Saunders Co., Philadelphia, 632 p.

Costello, D.P., M.E. Davidson, A. Eggers, M.H. Fox and C. Henley. 1957. *Methods of Obtaining and Handling Marine Eggs and Embryos,* Lancaster Press, Inc., Pennsylvania, 247 p.

Edmonds, C.H. 1946. *Reef and Shore Fauna of Hawaii,* Bishop Museum, special pub. 22, Honolulu, Hawaii, 381 p.

Fishelson, L. 1964. Observations and experiments of the Red Sea anemones and their symbiotic fish *Amphiprion bicinctus,* Contributions to the Knowledge of the Red Sea, 31, p. 3-16.

Freudenthal, H., J. Lee and J. McLaughlin. 1966. Some Symbionts of the Sea, Natural History, 25 (9), p. 46-51.

Henry, M. (editor). 1966. *Symbiosis,* vol. 1, Academic Press, New York, 478 p.

Hyman, L. 1940-51. *Invertebrates,* vol. 1-5, McGraw-Hill Co., New York.

Lutz, F., P. Welch, P. Galtsoff, J. Needham. 1937. *Cutlure Methods for Invertebrate Animals,* Dover Pub., Inc., New York, 590 p.

Miner, R. 1950. *Field Book of Seashore Life,* G.P. Putman's Sons, New York, 888 p.

Walterman, T. 1960. *The Physiology of Crustacea,* vol. 1, Academic Press, New York, 670 p.

CHAPTER 5

MARINE FISH

Several recent publications on the subject of salt water aquariums contain superb photographs of many marine fish; others have highlighted the more popular aquarium species. Few, if any, discuss pertinent facts and suggestions leading to the successful maintenance of marine fish. It is the hope of the author to contribute in a small way to the available literature, and to expand the underlying principles and dispel some popular misconceptions of fish culturing.

Habitats and Distribution

Those species of fish suitable for the marine aquarium have a wide distribution throughout the tropical seas and are similar in that they usually inhabit intertidal waters to maximum depths of l00 feet. Many of these fish inhabit the territory which is in close proximity to the continental shelf, and therefore are not found further than approximately 4 miles from shore. Otherwise, their habitats differ in respect to temperature, salinity, and the existant flora and fauna indigenous to the specific areas.

The continental shelf is a sloping shallow water area extending from the shore line to a point where it sharply descends to the ocean bottom. Most marine fish inhabit this area because of the abundance of food and shelter. Fish which abound in tropic waters usually frequent the coral reefs, which grow upon the continental shelf. The shelf itself may vary greatly in width depending on the geographic location. The southeastern side of Florida, for example, has a narrow shelf, due to erosion by the fast flowing Gulf Stream, while the west side has a broad shelf. Most marine aquarium species which come from the Atlantic are from the region off the coast of Florida and some from the coast of South America in the Caribbean Sea. In general, the surface salinities of the Atlantic waters, near the Florida coast are 33-36°/oo, with surface temperatures of 25-29° C. The Caribbean Sea (West Indies) has salinities and temperatures similar to those found off the coast of Florida.

Areas, such as California, have a narrow continental shelf, bordered by rocky banks. Here the reef fish must inhabit coastal areas with turbulent qualities. Many fish in this area are pelagic or free swimming in the open sea. The surface salinities in the Pacific are approximately 34°/oo with surface temperatures of 20-25° C., and as one moves westward toward Hawaii and the equatorial waters, the surface salinities rise to some of the highest values for the Pacific; 36°/oo with surface temperatures of 25° C. The Hawaiian Islands do not have numerous coral reefs since climatic and physical conditions in early eras did not favor their development. The reefs that are present are at depths of 20-30 feet and are small in size. In these reefs one can find the familiar surgeon fishes (Acanthuridea), butterfly fish (Chaetodontidae), squirrel fish (Holocentridae) and wrasses (Labridae). These families inhabit clear water free of suspended sediment and pollution. As would be suspected, much of the Hawaiian shore is composed of lava rock which is sometimes ground into a fine black sand by heavy wave action. Still further west towards Japan and China, the Pacific Ocean has surface temperatures of approximately $22°$ C. and surface salinities of approximately $35°/oo$. One must keep in mind that there is a great deal of fluctuation in this area depending on the season. For instance, in May, the surface salinity is $35°/oo$ and drops to $32°/oo$ in August. The area of the South Pacific is perhaps best known and includes the fabulous Australian reefs, the surface salinities here are approximately $35°/oo$ with surface temperatures of $20-25°$ C.

The Red Sea is said to contain a wealth of marine fishes. It bounds on the African continent, and while quite narrow, its shores are bordered by broad reef populated shelves, which are approximately 100 feet deep and then the sea drops to depths of 6000 feet directly or to other reefs 1500 feet deep and then to the bottom. Although there are many layered currents in the Red Sea, a rough approximation of salinities of surface waters is $40°/oo$ with temperatures on the surface of $22°$ C. South of the Red Sea lies the smallest of the "Great" oceans, the Indian Ocean. This encompasses the Mauritius and Madagascar Islands; both of which are known for their beautiful varieties of marine fish. The difficulties of importing fish from these distant areas are many. The salinities in the Indian Ocean are approximately $35°/oo$ with surface temperatures of $15-25°$ C. A large portion of the Indian Ocean borders on the Pacific Ocean and is referred to as the Indo-Pacific.

Though marine tropical fish inhabit several major regions, it is interesting to note that few of these fish are endemic to these regions. Endemic refers to those fish confined to a specific area and not found elsewhere. Many of the fish inhabiting the Indo-Pacific area, which happens to contain one of the richest communities of marine life, are found in many other places. Other fish, a considerably smaller number, are strictly indigenous to this area. The Hawaiian Islands which harbor several distinct species of reef fish have more than 30% of their population endemic to the region. This is probably due to the complex, jagged shore line and numerous islands and inlets which have provided ample opportunities for evolution. Strikingly, the inshore reefs of

Hawaii lack any groupers and snappers which comprise a dominant fraction of reef fishes in other areas.

A young nurse shark, *Ginglymostoma cirriatum* (photo credit: John G. Shedd Aquarium)

Clingfish and sea urchin. Clingfish have an anterior sucker. (photo credit: D. Faulkner)

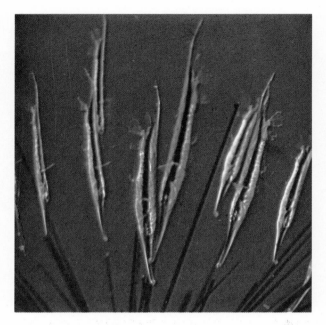

Aeoliscus strigatus, The shrimpfish will often
swim about feeding in a vertical position.
(photo credit: D. Faulkner)

Sargassum fish, *Histrio histrio*, a master of camouflage.
(photo credit: D. Faulkner)

Taenianotus triacanthus
(photo credit: D. Faulkner)

The Marine Fish

Marine fishes which are commonly kept in aquariums all belong to the Class Osteichthyes, the true bony fish. Some unusual fish, the sharks and rays, belong to the Class Chondrichthyes. These fish are not often kept in aquaria due to their large size, which can be quite lengthy even in juvenile stages. These fish also excrete large amounts of urea, which makes their presence in the average aquarium a hazard to themselves and other members. There are several orders of Osteichthyes which are commonly kept in marine aquaria, the largest number of which belong to the order Perciformes. This order of fish represents approximately 75% of the marine aquarium fish, most of which are highly prized and sought-after species. Other orders of fish mentioned in this chapter are the Tetraodontiformes, which includes the trigger fishes, file fishes, porcupine fishes, trunk fishes, and puffers, the order Beryciformes: the soldier fishes and squirrel fishes, and the order Gasterosteriformes, the sea horses and pipe fish.

CLASSIFICATION
Berg (1940)

Class Chondrichthyes

    Subclass Elasmobranchii

        Order Squaliformes

            Family Squalidae—dogfish shark
            Family Orectolobidae—nurse shark

Class Osteichthyes

    Order Perciformes

        Suborder Percoidei

            Family Chaetodontidae—butterfly fishes
            Family Labridae—wrasses
            Family Pomacentridae—damsel fishes
            Family Scaridae—parrot fishes
            Family Ephippidae—spade fishes
            Family Apogonidae—cardinal fishes
            Family Priacanthidae—big eyes

        Suborder Acanthuroidei

            Family Zanclidae—moorish idol
            Family Acanthuridae—surgeon fishes

        Suborder Gobioidei

            Family Gobiidae—gobies

        Suborder Cottoidei

            Family Scorpaenidae—scorpion fishes

    Order Tetraodontiformes

            Family Balistidae—trigger fishes and file fishes
            Family Ostraciidae—trunk fishes
            Family Tetraodontidae—puffers
            Family Diodontidae—porcupine fishes

    Order Gasterosteiformes

        Suborder Syngnathoidei

            Family Syngnathidae—sea horses and pipe fishes

    Order Beryciformes

            Family Holocentridae—squirrel fishes

Chaetodon ornatissimus, The clown butterfly fish
(photo credit: D. Faulkner)

Chaetodon melanotus
(photo credit: D. Faulkner)

Chaetodon vagabundus
(photo credit: D. Faulkner)

Chaetodon striatus, The banded butterfly fish
(photo credit: D. Faulkner)

Class Osteichthyes
Order Perciformes
Family Chaetodontidae: butterfly fishes and angel fishes
   This family represents many of the prized aquarium species. Their distribution is widespread in tropical areas although the most beautiful species are found in the Indo-Pacific regions.
   The angel fish are pugnacious and for this reason only one of these fish per aquarium is an advisable situation. If different-sized fish are kept in the same aquarium, usually they will not fight, while fish of approximately the same size will. Ample coral or rock should be supplied since they will provide shelter for the weaker individuals. Protection of life in nature involves camouflage, mimicry, and color changes. The angel fishes color changes remarkably during their growth. Most of these changes involve the loss of stripes, which are an indication of juvenile stages. The pattern of these stripes has been thought to provide protection from predators who at first glance do not realize the direction in which the immature fish is swimming. Many fish at earlier stages of growth have brightly colored tails which detract the predator's attention from the more vulnerable areas of the prey. Juvenile angel fish often have a prominent stripe on or near their tails, whereas the head region is devoid of any coloration. This lack of color

Red Sea Butterfly Fish, *Chaetodon falcula,*
(photo credit: R. Valenti)

Red Sea Butterfly fish, *Chaetodon semilarvatus,*
(photo credit: R. Valenti)

decreases the possiblity of attack to the head region and focuses attention on the less important posterior regions. The smaller specimens of angel fish are preferred for the marine aquarium as they are more colorful, more likely to acclimate to their new surroundings, and due to their size, more fish can be added to the aquarium.

The butterfly fish form the other most popular group of aquarium fish. These fish are quite different from the angel fish in that they are not territorially oriented and most are found moving in small groups of six to ten fish. The four-eyed butterfly fish, Chaetodon capistratus, are most often found in pairs. Butterfly fish also differ in that they lack spines which are seen on the pre-operculum (gill covers) of the angel fish. These spines are used as a defensive weapon by the angel fish to ward off adversaries. Butterfly fish are usually more shy than angel fish and therefore, are more difficult to feed. Some of the butterfly fish prefer specific invertebrates such as live or frozen corals (see feeding chart). Their fastidious feeding habits, however, should not deter the marine aquarist from keeping several of these colorful fish. Butterfly fish also use camouflage to trick predators. They, too, have color patterns on their posterior areas which could confuse an aggressive adversary. The four-eyed butterfly fish, Chaetodon capistratus, has a black patch of color near its tail. This spot resembles an eye and tends to lure predators from attacking the more anterior areas.

Chaetodon speculum
(photo credit: D. Faulkner)

Chaetodon rafflesi
(photo credit: D. Faulkner)

Chaetodon bennetti
(photo credit: D. Faulkner)

Platax pinnatus, although this is an extremely
handsome fish, it is not as hardy as *P. orbicularis.*
(photo credit: Marine Tropical Imports, Inc.)

Heniochus acuminatus, A species resembling, very much, The Moorish idol, *Zanclus sp.,* (photo credit: John G. Shedd Aquarium)

Pygoplites diacanthus,
Regal angelfish
(photo credit: R. Valenti)

Pomacanthus semicirculatus,
juvenile specimen.
(photo credit: D. Faulkner)

Potter's angelfish
Centropyge potteri,
(photo credit: D. Faulkner)

Centropyge argi,
The pigmy angelfish
(photo credit: D. Faulkner)

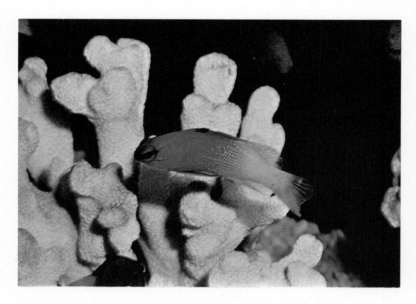

Gramma loreto, a fairy basslet which grows to over 3 inches
and is most commonly found in caves or under ledges.
(photo credit: R. Valenti)

Holocanthus tricolor, The rock beauty often grows to a large size in the aquarium. (photo credit: D. Faulkner)

A mature queen angelfish,*Holocanthus ciliaris.*

Pomacanthus arcuatus, the black angelfish
(photo credit: D. Faulkner)

Many of the butterfly fish have long tubular mouths which are an advantage in obtaining food in and among the coral. For many years, the long snout of one of the butterfly fish caused it to be confused with the fresh water archer fish.

As a rule the butterfly fish are peaceful, although Forcipiger longirostris, the longnose butterfly fish, is known to use its dorsal spines in an aggressive nature against other fish. Many other species of butterfly fish use their dorsal spines for defense.

Family Pomacentridae: damsel fishes and clown fishes

The damsel fish and clown fish are all small, colorful, reef fishes. There are many species of this family which thrive well when placed in the same tank with each other. Small groups of 5-30 individuals can be maintained easily. Many of the damsel fish are notorious "fin nippers" but if enough tank space is available this problem can be avoided. Their distribution is widespread in tropical seas. The color patterns of a certain percentage of these fish are different when immature and leads to much confusion when the systematic biologist attempts to classify them. Damsel fish and clown fish are usually not fussy eaters and become tame enough to take food from the surface of the water. A few of these fish have been spawned in aquaria. The critical standard that is necessary in initiating spawning is to obtain a sexually mature pair, and then provide them with the optimum water conditions (see section on breeding).

Whether or not anemones are kept with clown fish is a matter of taste rather than necessity. While it is true that anemones flourish in the presence of clown fish (see Chapter 4), the reverse situation is not necessarily true. Most large anemones provide a certain haven for clown fish in that they can retreat to the stinging tentacles and suffer no adverse effects, and the base of the anemone also provides spawning sites for the clown fish during breeding season. Oddly enough, the clown fish are not prejudiced by the origin of the anemones. Therefore one can have Florida fish living happily with Indo-Pacific anemones.

The damsel fish are aggregating fish and as is true of most aggregating fish, they are less hardy than are the non-schooling species. Many of the small damsel fish are often found swimming above coral heads in small aggregations and upon the approach of a diver, will seek refuge among the coral's crevices. The diver can then either pick up the entire piece of coral, if it is small enough, put it in a plastic collecting bag or squirt an annoying substance into the crevices to force out the fish. Needless to say, those collectors using substances such as formaldehyde to catch fish can cause serious damage.

Pomacanthus imperator showing the adult pigment pattern.
(photo credit: Marine Tropical Imports, Inc.)

Red sea Butterfly Fish
(photo credit: R. Valenti)

Amphiprion xanthurus This fish is shown in close
association with an anemone,
(photo credit: D. Faulkner)

Amphiprion xanthurus, notice the different coloration of this
fish from the accompanying photo of another *A. xanthurus.*
(photo credit: D. Faulkner)

Amphiprion percula, The most common clown fish.
(photo credit: D. Faulkner)

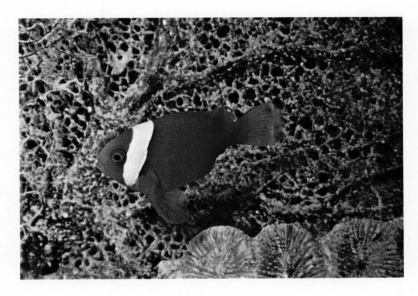

Amphiprion frenatus, the red clown fish.
(photo credit: Marine Tropical Imports, Inc.)

Black and Gold damselfish from New Caledonia
(photo credit: D. Faulkner)

Abudefdul coeruleus, the blue devil
(photo credit: D. Faulkner)

Pomacentrus violascens, a small hardy damselfish.
(photo credit: Marine Tropical Imports, Inc.)

98

Chromis rollandi
(photo credit: D. Faulkner)

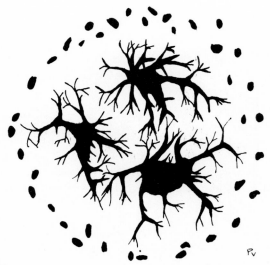

Diagram XIII

Pigment cells: These cells are able to expand (center) or contract (periphery) making it possible for a fish or invertebrate to increase or decrease the intensity of their coloration.

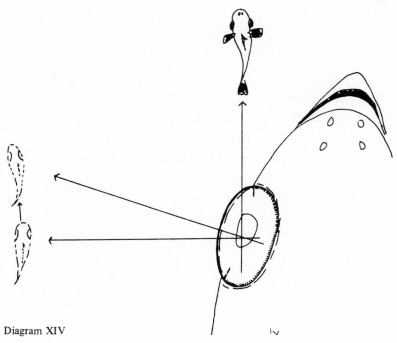

Diagram XIV

Fish see clearer in their forward visual field than they do in their lateral visual field. (based on N.B. Marshal)

Family Labridae: wrasses

The wrasses present an interesting and diverse behavioral study more so than any other family of fish. Many blend so completely with the substrate that they cannot be seen; some burrow beneath the sand and only their heads protrude; others at night, will rest on their sides and contour their bodies to any slight depression in the sand; still others, taking advantage of their wiry body construction, will crawl in between the "limbs" of the decorative coral pieces. Again, there is a great deal of confusion regarding classification since the color patterns of the immature fish differ from the adult. Thalassoma bifasciatus, the blue-head wrasse, is a prime example of the different color patterns in a life cycle. Juvenile males and females and mature female wrasses are pale yellow with vertical dark brown stripes and a non-forked tail; while the mature male displays a bright blue anterior region and forked tail. The beautiful Indo-Pacific twin spot wrasse, Coris angulata, shows a great deal of variation in color patterns in young and adult specimens, the younger fish being more highly colored.

Interestingly, many of these fish have an intrinsic timing device, a

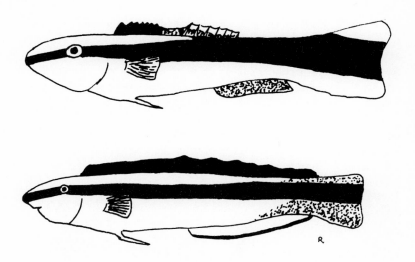

Diagram XV

MIMICRY: *Labroides dimidiatus,* the cleaner wrasse (top), is imitated
  by *Spidonotus taeniatus,* a predatory blenny (bottom).

"biological clock", which is often found in vertebrates and
invertebrates. These clocks are cyclic, rhythmic patterns that may be
manifested daily, monthly, or yearly. The internal clock of Coris
gaimard, which is usually collected in the North Pacific ocean, causes
the fish to regulate its normal cycle of rising (from beneath the gravel)
in early morning, scrounging for food during the day, and in the
evening retiring to the rocky substrate. Unfortunately, for the gaimard,
the time system of the collection site often varies with the time system
of his final destination. The Coris gaimard will continually try to
maintain the rigid schedule of its original habitat. (This geomagnetic
phenomenon is not affected by temperature and/or light.) For this
reason do not be surprised if the C. gaimard rises in the evening and
burrows beneath the sand in the morning. In most cases, he will forage
enough nutrients to maintain his existence.

  This family of fishes also includes the small, horizontally striped,
brightly colored, cleaning wrasse, Labroides dimidiatus. L. dimidiatus
spends much of its time participating in a symbiotic relationship with
other, often larger, fish. The little cleaning wrasse with his sharply
tapered head will thrust himself into the gills or inside the mouth of a
larger fish in search of parasites or adhering morsels of debris. The
larger fish readily sense the attributes of the wrasse and will hold open
their gill covers or mouths to permit the little fish to do its job. At

101

night, these small wrasses secrete a mucous cocoon which envelops them, while they sleep. The layers of mucous are sticky and therefore any loose particles of debris, even microscopic animals will adhere to this coating. The secondary function of the cocoon is the protection it affords the sleeping animal. The envelope mutes the bright colors of the wrasse so that the enmeshed fish blends well with substrate and coral.

The wrasses are non-schooling fishes possessing well developed canine teeth; some of the larger individuals can be very aggressive. For this reason, it is best to keep only smaller individuals of sizes from 1-4 inches.

Labroides phthirophagus
(photo credit: D. Faulkner)

Rainbow wrasse, *Labroides phthirophagus,*
removing parasites from, *Gymnothorax eurostus*
(photo credit: D. Faulkner)

Pescodorychthis frontalis, The chinese fish.
(photo credit: D. Faulkner)

Gomphosus varius, The birdfish
(photo credit: R. Valenti)

Wrasses are both colorful and hardy, however, they
can be pugnacious.
(photo credit: Marine Tropical Imports, Inc.)

Red Sea Wrasse
(photo credit: R. Valenti)

Clown wrasse, *Halichoeres radiatus,* Atlantic Ocean.
(photo credit: D. Faulkner)

A large parrot fish showing coral
crushing teeth.
(photo credit: R. Valenti)

Novaculichthys taeniourus collected in the Red Sea
compliments: (photo credit: R. Valenti)

Coris angulata, An adult twinspot wrasse
(photo credit: R. Valenti)

Family Scaridae: parrot fishes

Parrot fish, of the genus <u>Callyodon</u>, bear their descriptive name well, in that their teeth are fused and protrude resembling a beak. Some groups of the parrot fish lack this beak and the teeth are separated; these representatives belong to the genus <u>Leptoscarus</u>. In nature, these fish use their powerful beaks to break off pieces of coral or even to chew crabs or clams. Though parrot fish can be classified as herbivorous and will eat algae growing in the tank, they also will eat small invertebrates. In some cases, depending on the area from which they have been collected, they will eat mostly algae and little else. At night, they too secrete a mucous layer, which acts as a protective device for their bodies. Most of the parrot fish are too large (3-5 feet long) to be kept in an aquarium, but smaller specimens are easily maintained.

Color patterns of parrot fish often change as the fish matures and large differences in color patterns are shown between males and females. Dr. L. Schultz has managed to reduce the 350 different parrot fish to a smaller group of 80 species.

Platax orbicularis, the batfish
(photo credit: D. Faulkner)

107

Family Ephippidae: batfishes

The batfish, a member of the Ephippidae, commonly called the spadefish, are highly prized possessions to members of the aquarium world. (batfish are often classified as belonging to the family Platacidae). These fish are solitary individuals and are found in pelagic areas. They will adapt quickly to the aquarium and are so tame they quickly learn to take food from the aquarist's fingers. While they become as large as 20 inches, tank specimens should not exceed 7-8 inches; at this size, they are not belligerent with smaller fish.

These fish appear delicate as they have beautiful diaphonous fins that greatly add to the overall size of the animal. Often, the fins will shred due to abrasions on rocks. The fins are used as a diversion for predators, and many specimens can be seen lacking 50% of their fins after fighting.

They will eat small portions of food frequently and they are not particularly fussy eaters. Natives often catch batfish on hook and line using a piece of banana. For the aquarist who feels he should vary the diet of the batfish, a small piece of banana can be fed.

The Big Eye, prefers dimly lighted aquariums.
(photo credit: R. Valenti)

Family Apogonidae: cardinal fish

The cardinal fish are, as a group, both beautiful and delicate. Most of these species are collected in Floridian and Caribbean waters. They are often so small, 2-4 inches, that when placed in the aquarium, care should be exercised to provide them with ample hiding places.

In nature, cardinal fishes make up an important part of the food chain due to their abundance and the aquarist should take care that this does not occur in his tank.

These fish are mouth breeders, and the male carries the fertilized eggs in his mouth until they hatch. Cardinal fish are not difficult to feed and will take bites of dried food from the surface of the water. They are very greedy and often fill their mouths with large pieces of undigested food.

Although not in the same family, the Big-Eye or Conchfish, are often grouped with the cardinal fish because of their similarities. They are actually members of the family Priacanthidae according to Berg's classification (1940). These fish prefer dimly lit aquariums and are active only at night. Care should be taken not to over illuminate the tank as it may cause blindness of the fish. If the tank is illuminated during the day, the Big-Eyes should be fed during the night when they are most active.

Apogon nematopterus
(photo credit: D. Faulkner)

109

Suborder: Acanthuroidei

Family Zanclidae: the Moorish idol

This group is represented by the highly esteemed Moorish idol. Although it was once considered difficult to keep alive, poor water quality was probably the reason for its quiet demise. They are usually collected from the Indian Ocean and the strenuous trip to the States has often proved fatal. Aquarists attempting to keep these fish should keep water with a salinity of 36 °/oo and provide algae and brine shrimp.

A great deal of speculative interest has been shown in the horned and non-horned specimens of this fish. The lack of horns appears to merely indicate the juvenile form of Z. cornutus

Closely resembling this species is one of the butterfly fish, Heniochus acuminatus. Heniochus is a very hardy, attractive fish that is easily sustained under aquarium conditions. The resemblance between the Moorish idol and the Heniochus is striking but they are two different suborders. These fish should not be grouped with overly aggressive fish as their fins will shred easily from any slight altercation.

Zebrasoma flavescens, This species has a gray-green color phase, The cleaner wrasse L. *phthirophagus* is shown removing parasites (photo credit: D. Faulkner)

Zebrasoma veliferum, the sailfin tang
(photo credit: D. Faulkner)

Acanthurus xanthopterus, from the Red Sea
(photo credit: R. Valenti)

Family Acanthuridae: surgeon fish

The surgeon fish, well deserving the name "doctor-fish", have sharp, scalpel-like, spines on either side of the caudal peduncle. This spine is used defensively by this fish if it is annoyed. Some members of the surgeon fish family possess sharp poisonous spines on the dorsal and pelvic fins. These animals should be shown tender loving care and they, in turn, will be a fine aquisition.

Most of these fish are large (10-14 inches) but still they do well in aquariums. Unfortunately they are very aggressive and do establish a "pecking order" in which the largest fish bullies all the smaller fish, and the next largest has priority of being the next bully after the largest. Some surgeon fish, such as A. leucosternon, can be fussy eaters and

Acanthurus achilles, from Hawaii. A pearly jaw fish can be seen peering up from his hole in the sand.
(photo credit: R. Valenti)

Acanthurus achilles and jewlfish
(photo credit: R. Valenti)

prefer filamentous algae and bits of fresh scallop and live brine shrimp. Most surgeon-fish will not live on merely a protein diet and must be fed considerable amounts of algae.

Surgeon fish display a very strange "acronus" larval stage at which time they possess vertical ridges on their body. Following this, several species undergo radical color changes making identification of juveniles and adults difficult; geographical color variations are also common. The yellow tang, <u>Zebrasoma flavescens</u> is yellow in areas off Hawaii but is brown in the Indo-Pacific.

Suborder Gobioidei
Family Gobiidae: gobies

This group of small (2-3 inches), inconspicuous fish, usually prefer to seek refuge on the bottom of the tank rather than swim. There are more than 400 species of these fish making them the dominant family of fishes.

The neon goby, <u>Gobiosoma oceanops</u>, is the popular representative of this family for the marine aquarium. These small fish have a cylindrical,

Gobiosoma oceanops, The neon
goby, swimming above a live rose
coral. (photo credit: D. Faulkner)

tapered body construction, with blue and black horizontal stripes. They
are hardy, easily fed, and because they are small do not limit the
aquarist to a fewer number of fish. Characteristically, these fish often
spawn in the marine aquarium but little success has been met in rearing
the young. Of course, any large fish will quickly enjoy these fish as
tasty morsels. Ample amounts of coral or shells should be provided for
them to hide.

One species of goby forms a symbiotic relationship with a shrimp.
The shrimp digs out and maintains holes in the sand, which the goby
inhabits; in return the goby provides ample warning for the shrimp in
case a predator is lurking in the area. In the event of an attack they
both frequent the holes in the sand.

The most colorful of the gobies is the blue-banded goby, Lythrypnus
dalli. These California coastal residents are red with blue vertical stripes,
(see cover photo).

Suborder Cottoidei
Family Sorpaenidae: the lion fish

The scorpion fish or lion fish are the dramatically colored and well
known members of this family. The adults are often a foot long and for
this reason only the younger members should be purchased. These fish

Pterois sphex
(photo credit: D. Faulkner)

Pterois volitans
(photo credit: R. Valenti)

Pterois sp., The lion fish. In background is
a live sponge.
(photo credit: F. Perilla)

are carnivorous and will eat small chunks of meat and live fish. The
most forward of the dorsal spines are hollow, each containing a sack of
toxic poison at its base. In their natural habitat these fish are sluggish
and display their dorsal spines when threatened by a predator. They
make an attractive addition to the aquarium and will not harm other
fish unless they are small enough to be swallowed. The aquarist should
not tempt fate by brushing against the spines; if the spines puncture the
skin, there is a potential danger of a painful wound. Lion fish do not
like too much light and should be provided with a shaded portion of
the aquarium or an overturned shell. Most of the lion fish are found in
the Red Sea where the salinity is approximately 36-40°/oo.

An extremely deadly fish, the stonefish, Synanceja verrucosa, closely
resembles a small rock but if accidentaly stepped on will eject a
neurotoxic venom into the skin and cause death. Although related to
the lion fish it lacks any outstanding beauty.

Order Tetradontiformes
Family Balistidae: trigger fish

Trigger fish and file fish all have a large dorsal spine. The long dorsal
spine of the trigger fish can be locked in place by the erection of a

Balistes vetula, A queen trigger fish eating
a sea urchin. The sharp spines are first
nipped off exposing the fleshy interior
(photo credit: H. Pederson)

Odonus niger, the red fang trigger fish so named for
it's red canine teeth.
(photo credit: Marine Tropical Imports, Inc.)

Balistes, vetula, can be an aggressive fish and
should not be kept in a community
aquarium. (photo credit: R. Valenti)

Balistoides conspicillum the clown trigger fish,
one of the most expensive marine fishes
(photo credit: R. Valenti)

Lactoria cornulata, the long horned cowfish.
(photo credit: Marine Tropical Imports, Inc.)

Chilomycterus schoepfi, the striped burr fish. Grows
to 10" and is highly susceptible to disease organisms.
(photo credit: Marine Tropical Imports, Inc.)

second and smaller spine found behind and at the base of the larger spine. The trigger fish usually seek the security of corals for their slumber periods. The erection of the spine is used to wedge the fish firmly in place for the night, a time which finds most marine fish lying at the bottom of the reefs. Their metabolic rates decrease during periods of inactivity (like man), and therefore the "triggered" spine insures a certain amount of protection against the hazards of the deep. Species of trigger fish are found throughout the world but Balistoides conspicillum, the clown trigger fish, is the zenith of all marine possessions. In fact, it is often called "the most beautiful fish in the world" and for the possession of the "most..." it is also the most expensive.

While smaller members of this family can be kept in marine aquaria, larger fish (10-12 inches) tend to excrete tremendous amounts of wastes so there should be a limit to the amount of food they are permitted to consume. These fish enjoy morsels of live coral, crabs or other shelled invertebrates. It is extremely important that the larger members of this family or for that matter all large marine species should be underfed to some degree. Larger fish often will eat so much that efficient removal of their waste products, particularly ammonia, is impossible. Remember a fish in an aquarium is more confined and less active than in its natural environment, therefore, it is wiser to feed it less.

Common puffer fish from the Atlantic, shown just after having been buried in the sand. (photo credit: R. Valenti)

Family Tetraodontidae: puffer fish
Family Ostraciidae: trunk fish
Family Diodontidae: porcupine fish

These family names are represented respectively by the puffers, trunk fish and procupine fish. All are bizzare in shape; and have sluggish swimming and reaction patterns and therefore prefer to stay near the bottom or in close proximity to shelter. They eat crustaceans and small tidbits of scallop, and despite their naturally small stomachs, they can consume a phenomenally large amount of bulk. The puffers are extremely susceptible to the parasitic dinoflagellate, Oodinium, and are usually the first to contract this disease.

Puffers are well known for their ability to swallow air or water and thereby inflate themselves. This is a great help when encountering a hungry predator. Porcupine fish resemble puffers with the addition of spines covering the body. These spines are folded back while swimming but can be erected if agitated.

The trunk fishes form an interesting group of fish. Identification is difficult due to coloration patterns which vary widely from male to female. Some species of these fish have been reported to secrete a toxin capable of killing other tank inhabitants.

Although most species of puffers and trunk fish contain toxins they are considered a delicacy in many parts of the world, particularly in Japan and some Pacific Islands. In these areas only a licensed "fugu" cook can prepare these fish.

Squirrel fish from Hawaii, *Ostichthys, japonicus.*
(photo credit: D. Faulkner)

121

Squirrel fish from Hawaii
photo credit: R. Valenti)

Order Beryciformes
Family Holocentridae: squirrel fish

Squirrel fish reach a length of 10 inches and can do well in an aquarium if they are small. They are often shy and prefer sheltered corners, shells, or corals. They prefer dimly lighted areas, excessive illumination will irritate their protruding, unprotected eyes. Nature has given these fish larger eyes to compensate for the dim light they experience at their natural depths. They use to advantage their larger eyes as they become more active at night. Night is an opportune time for a food search since most of the other fish will be quietly subdued by sleep.

Squirrel fish as larvae are an important part of the plankton in many areas of the Pacific. As the squirrel fish mature, they become economically important as food fish.

Interestingly, squirrel fish are capable of producing sounds audible to the human ear without a hydrophone.

Order Gasterosteiformes
Family Syngnathidae: sea horses and pipe fishes

The sea horses and pipe fish, like the trunk fish, have a hard, often colorful, external skeleton. They are quiet hardy but due to their fussy eating habits and large amounts of excretory products, these fish do well as the sole inhabitants of a tank. They prefer live brine shrimp,

Hippocampus hudsonius, these fish should be
provided with branches to which they can attach.
(photo credit: R. Valenti)

either newly hatched or adult, depending on the size of the sea horses
themselves. They must be provided with branch coral or other finely
branched structures so that their prehensile (monkey-like) tails can curl
around these projections for stabilization. Male sea horses and pipe fish
have pouches into which the females transfer fertilized eggs to be
incubated. After approximately 25 days, the males experience labor
pains as they release their live progeny. The breeding of most sea horses
is not an uncommon occurrence. Actually, most sea horses are not
mated in captivity but instead, gravid males are collected. Freshly
hatched brine shrimp should be provided for the young. Pipe fish
breeding is difficult as the progeny will not survive unless microscopic
food organisms are available.

The small pigmy, Hippocampus zosterae, 1½ inches long when full
grown, is the hardiest of the sea horses. These, contrary to other sea
horses, can be bred and raised in an aquarium. Care should be exercised
that excessive bubbling from air stones does not occur in an aquarium
with these animals since the males will often draw water into their
pouches. If air enters, they will lose equilibrium.

Foods for Marine Fish

Proper nutrition is of the utmost importance in maintaining and
displaying marine fish. Poorly nourished fish are exposed to stress
which results in lowering their level of resistance to disease. Nutrition is
also significant in maintaining proper pigmentation of aquarium
specimens and preventing a loss of intensity of this coloration.

Marine fish are either carnivorous, in which case they eat a majority of animal protein, herbivorous, meaning they eat mainly plant material, or omnivorous in which case they eat both plant and animal material in approximately equal proportions. The difficulty of providing a proper diet for marine fish can be better understood when one sees the specific food organisms required by both carnivores and herbivores.

It would be difficult for the aquarist to try and duplicate the food normally consumed by each species of fish contained within an aquarium and it is also not essential. Almost all carnivorous marine fish will thrive on a staple diet rich in proteins, fats, carbohydrates and minerals. A proper diet such as this can be provided by feeding quantities of crabmeat, scallop and shrimp which are easily obtained from a local fish market. Herbivorous fish can be maintained by providing a similar diet with the addition of plant material. It is interesting that many herbivorous fish when confined to an aquarium will actively feed upon animal protein, something which they will not do in their natural environment. The plant material offered to herbivores can either be blue green algal mats which can be grown within the aquarium or pieces of ulva and/or chopped spinach.

It is known that a predominance of red yellow and orange pigmentation of marine fish is caused by carotenoid pigments. These carotenoid compounds are not synthesized "De Novo" but rather are acquired through feeding on certain crustaceans and algae. For this reason it is essential in order to maintain intense coloration of fish within an aquarium, that a good growth of algae be provided for the fish to feed upon. It would also be beneficial to provide fish with a prepared fish food which contains carotenoid compounds.

Gaterin lineatus, Sweet lips from the Indo-Pacific, (photo credit: D. Faulkner)

Live brine shrimp, if rinsed in fresh sea water several times before serving to the fish, is a good food. Note well, when copper is being used as a treatment do not feed brine shrimp to fish (see chapter 6, copper). For a flavorful variation use the planktonic copepod (see chapter 4, arthropods) *Calanus finmarchicus,* it is prepared as a paste and provides an excellent source of proteins and other nutrients as well as providing dietary variation. The old rule which says fish grow faster if fed smaller portions frequently rather than one or two large feedings is worthwhile advice.

The use of amino acid and vitamin additives to aquarium water is not a new technique but it is highly important and often neglected. The amino acids: Arganine, Alanine, Glutamic Acid, and Aspartic Acid are normally found in sea water in the natural environment but dissipate quickly in closed systems. Since these amino acids are often beneficial in stimulating the appetite of both fish and invertebrates it is advisable to add small amounts to the aquarium water (already prepared solutions can be purchased from most dealers handling marine organisms but care must be taken in that this material will not remain potent if not refrigerated). The appetite stimulating effect that this material will have on specific fish or invertebrates will vary greatly and in most cases the desired effect will take several days to occur.

Vitamins like amino acids are extremely important in nutrition and like amino acids will not persist for long periods of time in the

Cromileptes altivelis, the panther fish, one of many Indo-Pacific groupers.
(photo credit: Marine Tropical Imports, Inc.)

aquarium. It therefore becomes advisable to add specific vitamins to the aquarium water to aid the organisms being maintained. Care must be taken not to add too much of any vitamin since many bacteria will bloom in the presence of specific vitamins. The chart below lists important vitamins and deficiency syndromes. The use of human vitamin tablets in the marine aquarium is often quite successful. The method usually used is one high potency vitamin tablet per 50 gallons of aquarium water.

Vitamin	Deficiency Syndromes
THIAMIN	Poor appetite, poor growth, convulsions, edema.
RIBOFLAVIN	Hermorrhagic eyes, abnormal eye pigmentation, cloudy lenses, poor appetite, poor growth.
PYRIDOXINE	Nervous disorders, poor appetite, epileptiform fits, anemia.
PANTOTHENIC	Clubbed gills, sluggishness, poor growth.
INOSITOL	Poor growth, skin lesions, distended stomachs.
BIOTIN	Loss of appetite, muscle atrophy, poor growth
FOLIC ACID	Poor growth, lethargy, dark coloration.
CHOLINE	Poor growth, poor food conversion.
NICOTINIC ACID	Loss of appetite, poor growth.
VITAMIN B_{12}	Poor appetite.
ASCORBIC ACID	Eye lesions, Hemorrhagic skin.

FOOD CHART

FAMILY	REPRESENTATIVES	FOOD
Squalidae Orectolobidae	dogfish shark nurse shark	Small pieces of scallop or other meats, live fish, earthworms. Size of food should never be larger than ½ the size of the fish's mouth. Carnivorous; generally poor eaters.
Scorpaenidae Chaetodontidae Zanclidae Balistidae Ephippidae	scorpion fishes, lion fish butterfly fishes, angel fish moorish-idol trigger fish bat fish	Scallop, beef heart, liver, live brine shrimp, freeze dried foods, white worms, tubifex pieces of live coral, and algae. Omnivorous: angel fish-good eaters, butterfly fish—poor eaters (generally). Moorish idol—poor eaters. Trigger fish—good eaters. Lion fish-good eaters.
Labridae Gobiidae	wrasses gobies	Same as Chaetodontidae except pieces of food should be smaller and brine shrimp should be emphasized. Omnivorous: generally good eaters.
Pomacentridae	damsel fish	Live brine shrimp, grated pieces of scallop and beef heart. Freeze dried shrimp also readily eaten. Pieces of *Ulva* or other algae should be provided. Omnivorous: generally good eaters.
Scaridae	parrot fish	Pieces of live coral, crustaceans such as clams or mussels can be tried. Much of their diet should be algae. Omnivorous: good eaters.

FOOD CHART (continued)

FAMILY	REPRESENTATIVES	FOOD
Acanthuridae	surgeon fish	At young stages, they should be fed similarly to damsel fish but adults are more herbivorous and must be provided with algae. Omnivorous: good eaters.
Apogonidae	cardinal fish	Should be fed similarly to damsel fish but size of food should depend on the size of fish's mouth. Omnivorous: good eaters.
Holocentridae	squirrel fish	Should be fed similarly to damsel fish, however, feeding should not be done in the brightly lighted aquarium. Omnivorous: fair eaters.
Ostraciidae Tetraodontidae Diodontidae	trunk fish puffers porcupine fish	Should be fed scallop, invertebrates such as crabs, shrimp and clams. Omnivorous: good eaters.

TYPES OF FOODS USED BY CARNIVORES

I   SESSILE ANIMALS: animals which adhere to the substrate of the ocean such as sponges, tube worms and corals. Examples of carnivorous fish which feed on sessile animals: Butterfly fish and angel fish.

II   Shelled Invertebrates: Clams, oysters, scallops and gastropods. Examples of carnivores feeding on shelled invertebrates: Trunkfish, porcupinefish, pufferfish and some wrasses.

III   Zooplankton: consists of the animal portion of plankton (pterepods, crustaceans) in contrast to the phytoplankton which is the plant portion of plankton. Examples of carnivores feeding on zooplankton: many damselfish.

IV   Ectoparasites: consist mainly of copepods which parasitize fish. Examples of carnivores feeding upon ectoparasites: some gobies and juvenile angelfish.

V   Fish: which are small enough to be devoured by larger or more aggressive carnivores. Example of carnivores feeding on fish: Groupers, frogfish, lionfish and snake eels.

TYPES OF FOODS USED BY HERBIVORES

I   Symbiotic algae: Zooxanthele which are symbionts of coral and anemones.

II   Phytoplankton: plant portion of plankton. Fed upon by many juvenile fish.

III Algal mats and anchored plants.

Number of Fish per Aquarium

It has always seemed remarkable to me how empirical values for a certain number of fish per gallon per tank have been computed. If the aquarium is chemically balanced it is difficult to set a limit on the number of fish one can keep in it. What is the maximum number of fish for an aquarium? This question is answered by asking another question...How much time and concern is the aquarist willing to contribute to the marine endeavor? If the dedication is small, then limit the number of fish (1 fish/2 gallons water). An excellent filtration system will facilitate the aquarist's venture and therefore more fish can be stocked. As long as the fish do not rise to the surface gasping for air this is a good sign that the fish are not overcrowded. The best sign one might use to note overcrowding is clouding of the water after the fish are fed. Directly after feeding or before, many fish excrete their wastes and this is the time a problem of overcrowding may show up. Solve this problem by either purchasing a larger, more efficient filtering mechanism or keeping fewer fish.

Freudian Factor

Marine fish are generally quite hardy as is well proven by their ability to survive the traumas of collection, transportation, and lastly, adaptation to a new time sequence and habitat. Once they are introduced into the aquarium they are faced with a problem of survival; namely, adapt to the new environment and assume, or be placed by other community members, into a social niche. The term "Freudian Factor" refers to the psychological aspect of the fish's ability to adapt to a new environment and the response of the fish to their handling procedures. The shock of being captured and then placed in a temporary holding tank and then being shipped to an importer until they are sold to a retail store, and finally, mercifully, being purchased by the aquarist can be a huge hurdle for fish to overcome and survive swimmingly.

The fish when first introduced into the aquarium should be permitted to rest; this involves dim lighting for the first day, assurance of certain hiding places, and no food (unless the fish seems anxious to eat and extremely thin). Some fish are hungry immediately which is a good sign of hardiness and heartiness. If possible do not immediately introduce the new arrival into an already established aquarium since the elders of the fish community may pick on the newest member. With the addition of a new aquarium arrival, it is certain that any adhering parasites will thrive in the stable aquarium, so unhappily, anticipate the outbreak of some disease (see Chapter 6). After a few days the fish will begin to emerge from hiding in search of food which is a good index of adaptation to his new habitat.

Sexing Marine Fish

Many aquarists after admiring the beautiful, diverse representatives of marine fish are astonished at the high prices. These exorbitant prices are due to the accumulation of expenses up to the time the aquarist sees the fish. The first drop in the proverbial bucket is the cost of collecting and importing the fish. Logically, the Floridian species are far cheaper than the Red Sea fish. While the total answer to more reasonably priced fish is not through breeding them in captivity, known breeding responses and characteristics would be a significant contribution to the knowledge of the marine existence. Breeding in captivity will aid in understanding the life cycle of fish and their inherent weaknesses and thereby increase the selection of healthier strains of fish. Unfortunately, many marine fish are too big at the time of spawning, and too, a bigger problem is that many of the eggs are pelagic which means they must float freely on the ocean's surface and then slowly sink to certain depths before hatching. There are, however, two successfully spawning varieties of aquarium fish. Both of these species have been sexed and spawned in captivity.

The Neon Goby (G. oceanops)

The antiquated method of purchasing random fish as a means of obtaining a mating pair is haphazard and extremely expensive. The aquarist must not only meet the initial cost of more fishes than those which are necessary but he must also supply ample space for them. Adequate space is a necessity as mature males are belligerent and are

A male and female *Gobiosoma oceanops*. Note the white distended abdomen of the female, (left).

territorially oriented. It therefore becomes desirable to sexually differentiate species of these fish.

Neon gobies are sexually mature at approximately 1.3 inches. The males are usually larger fish with slightly longer fins and brighter colors. These characteristics, however, are not discerned easily and often it is impossible to distinguish between sexes using these criteria.

The one external characteristic which is of significant value is the color pattern in the caudal peduncle and caudal fin region. In the male, the black coloration that runs along the lateral surface of the fish's body and ends on the caudal fin, rises definitely at the terminal end of the pattern. The black pattern of the female will turn downwardly or remain straight at its terminal point. Another obvious difference pertaining to the black patterns on the lateral surface of the male fish is its broader nature in the region of the caudal peduncle as compared to the narrower coloration of the female.

A conclusive difference between the sexes in the neon gobies is the obvious protrusion of the female's abdominal region as the ovaries increase in size.

Clown fish (A. percula)

The clown fish was one of the first marine fishes to successfully spawn in a marine aquarium. Most accounts of the spawning procedure describe the mode of reproduction; few, if any, detail the sexing of these fishes. Sexual differentiation has been limited to a generalized statement that the males are smaller and more brightly colored than the females.

By comparing the gross external anatomy of mature (approximately 2 inches long) A. percula and the subsequent examination of their gonadal tissue, distinct macroscopic, sexually differentiating characteristics were noted.

A. percula have three distinct white bands, each of which are bordered with narrow black rims. The central band is triangular in shape and differs distinctly in males and females. The male fish has a broader and more pronounced central band than the female. The pattern of the broad central band in the male points sharply to the cranial region. The band in the female is not sharply accentuated, the projection is blunt and the central band is generally more narrow. A trait less discernable, though present, is the broader white band in the caudal peduncle of male fishes.

It is interesting that these distinctive band patterns are persistent in juvenile fish (approximately 1 inch long). Therefore, the selection of A. percula pairs is greatly facilitated by these characteristics.

Heniochus intermedius, showing cranial horn of female (6" long specimen). These are the first photos showing secondary sexual characteristics among these species. (photo credit: R. Valenti)

H. intermedius, close up of female.
(photo credit: R. Valenti)

H. intermedius, showing branched cranial
horn occurring in mature male specimens.
(photo credit: R. Valenti)

H. intermedius, close up of male.
(photo credit: R. Valenti)

A. percula Male (top) showing the broad central band;
female (bottom) with narrow central band.
(photo credit: R. Valenti)

MARINE FISH
BIBLIOGRAPHY

American Fisheries Society. 1970. *A list of Common and Scientific Name of Fishes from the United States and Canada.* Report of the Committee on Names of Fishes, 89th Annual Meeting, 102 p.

Axelrod, H. and W. Vorderwinkler. 1965. *Salt-Water Aquarium Fish,* T.F.H. Publications, Inc., New Jersey, 351 p.

Axelrod, H. and C. Emmens 1969. *Exotic Marine Fishes,* T.F.H. pub., Inc., N.J.

Böhlke, J. and C. Chaplin 1968. *Fishes of the Bahamas and Adjacent Tropical Waters,* Livingston Pub. Co., Pa. 769 p.

Braker, W. 1966. *Know How to Keep Saltwater Fishes.* The Pet Library LTD., 64 p.

Brown, M. (editor). 1957. *The Physiology of Fishes,* vol. I-II, Academic Press, New York.

Breder, C. and D. Rosen. 1966. *Modes of Reproduction in Fishes,* The Natural History Press, Garden City, New York, 941 p.

Cameron, A. and R. Endean. 1966. The venom apparatus of the scorpion fish, *Notesthes robusta,* Toxicon 4, p. 111-121.

Choat, H. 1966. Parrot fish, Australian Natural History, p. 265-258.

Engel, L. and the Editors of Life. 1963. *The Sea,* Time Inc., New York 190 p.

Feddern, H. 1965. The spawning growth and general behavior of the Bluehead wrasse, *Thalassoma bifasciatus,* Bulletin of Marine Science, 15 (4), p. 896-941.

Fishelson, L. 1963. Observations of the biology and behavior of Red Sea Coral Fishes, Contributions to the Knowledge of the Red Sea, 30, p. 11-26.

Fishelson, L. 1964. Observations and experiments on the Red Sea anemones and their symbiotic fish *Amphiprion bicinctus,* Contributions to knowledge of the Red Sea, 31, p. 3-16.

Gosline, W. and V. Brock. 1965. *Handbook of Hawaiian Fishes,* University of Hawaii Press, 371 p.

Greenwood, H., D. Rosen, S. Weitzman, and G. Myers. 1966. Phyletic studies of Teleostian Fishes, with provisional classification of living forms, Bulletin of the American Museum of Natural History, 131 (4) p. 339-456.

Henry, M. (editor). 1966. *Symbiosis,* vol I, Academic Press, New York, 478 p.

Herald, E. 1964. Cleaner fish for a cleaner aquarium, Pacific Discovery, 17 (6) p. 28-29.

Herald, E. 1965. *Living Fishes of the World,* Doubleday and Company, Inc., New York. 304 p.

Hoar, W.S. and D.J. Randall 1969. *Fish Physiology,* Academic Press, N.Y., vol. I-IV.

Lagler, K., J. Bardach, R. Miller. 1962. *Ichthylogy,* John Wiley and Sons, Inc. New York. 545 p.

Lewis, W. 1963. *Maintaining Fishes for Experimental and Instructional Purposes,* Southern Illinois University Press, 100 p.

Marshall, T. 1965. *Fishes of the Great Barrier Reef and Coastal Waters of Queensland,* Livingston Publishing Co., Pennsylvania, 566 p.

Nikolskii, G.V. 1961. *Special Ichthylogy,* translated from Russian, The Israel Program for Scientific Translations. 538 p.

Perlmutter, A. 1961. *Guide to the Marine Fishes,* New York University Press, New York, 431 p.

Randall, J. 1961. A contribution to the biology of the convict surgeonfish of the Hawaiian Islands, *Acanthurus triostegus sandvicensis,* Pacific Science, 15, p. 215-271.

Randall, J. 1967. Food habits of reef fishes of the West Indies, *Studies in Tropical Oceanography,* No. 5, 665-847.

Randal, J. 1968. *Caribbean Reef Fishes,* T.F.H. Pub., Inc., N.J., 318 p.

Straughan, R. 1956. Saltwater fishes are spawned, The Aquarium, p. 157-159.

Straughan, R. 1964. The *Salt-Water Aquarium in the Home,* A.S. Barnes and Co., New York, 304 p.

Valenti, R. 1967. Sexing *Amphiprion percula,* Salt Water Aquarium, 3 (3), p. 61.

Walters, V. 1959. *Salt Water Fish of Florida and the Southern Coasts.* Caribous Press, Bronxville, New York, 23 p.

CHAPTER 6

DISEASES OF MARINE FISH

No matter what consideration is given aquarium fishes and their synthetic environment, a tremendous strain exists until each faction becomes stabilized. The psychogenic ailments of fish, or those traumas caused mainly by psychological distress from physical changes in the environment, are always points of agitation. Since the fish and their environment are flexible parameters, each is capable of responding to stress. Response to the strain often results in weakening the fish's level of resistance. This rise in susceptability increases the possibility for parasite invasion of the host. Many parasites are present on healthy fish and any irregularity in the physical environment could lower the fish's resistance and thereby disrupt the delicate equilibrium that exists. This situation is similar to those circumstances that pervade man in his environment. Man's daily exposure to various aerial bacteria and viruses will not necessarily cause disease unless his resistance is lowered due to fatigue, poor diet, etc. The aquarist will find it difficult, if not impossible, to eliminate the possibility of epidemics especially if new fish are continually introduced into an establsihed community. The outbreak however can be minimized and checked by exercising certain precautions.

General Symptoms of Disease

Most fish are actively moving creatures and when diseased will manifest a limited range of observable symptoms. Loss of locomotion, or spastic, uncontrolled locomotion, is symptomatic that something is amiss. Many diseased fish will swim aimlessly, jerking back and forth, and some will swim in circular patterns. Often parasites adhere to external surfaces and the fish, seemingly, make a conscious effort to remove these organisms by scraping or brushing against rocks and substrate.

Lack of interest in food and a sluggish attitude at feeding time does not necessarily indicate disease. Often female fish fast while their ovaries mature since there is limited space in the abdominal cavity for both distended digestive tract and swollen, mature, ovaries. Also, many fish will exhibit a preference for a single food to the exclusion of all other foods even if it means starvation and death. (refer to Chapter V, section on feeding.)

Blanched color is a characteristic that denotes metabolic irregularities or circulatory deficiencies. Sporozoan infections as well as bacterial infections also account for a noticeable loss of color. Wan color may also be due to lack of sufficient oxygen or light. The observation of darkly pigmented, localized areas may suggest tumors or internal parasites.

The experienced aquarist, who is attuned to the behavior of fish and their problems of survival, will be alert to notice symptoms and any diagnostic hints of disease. By isolating the infected fish, the aquarist ensures the survival of both the afflicted and healthy members of the tank.

GILL INFECTIONS

Oodinium and the Use of Copper as a Treatment

Copper, a metal which can be lethal to fish and invertebrates, has been previously introduced to the marine aquarist as the most effective medication for the treatment of Oodinium spp. Its effectiveness against this prevalent marine dinoflagellate is quite obvious, but less observable are the deleterious effects it has on marine fish.

Oodinium, although present on many marine fish in their natural environment, seldom becomes a hazard under these circumstances. The check valve that alters the attachment and survival of the Oodinium in nature has many forms. These may involve low temperatures, low salinities, great depths at which many fish live, and too, the physiological hardiness of the fish.

Once a fish is removed from its natural environment and placed in an aquarium, it becomes much easier for the parasite to thrive. Often the parasitic stages are so numerous on the gill filaments that the vital exchange of gases is blocked and death results.

Formula for copper sulfate (pentahydrate) to yield .15 ppm in a marine aquarium (after Dempster and Shipman '69).

$$CuSO_4 \cdot 5H_2O = \frac{V \times 14.88 \times .15 \text{ ppm}}{1000}$$

V = Total volume, in gallons, of aquarium to be treated. 14.88 = constant.

Example: to yield .15 ppm in a 100 gallon aquarium:

$$Cu = \frac{100 \times 14.88 \times .15}{1000}$$

$CuSO_4$ = .22 grams/100 gallons of aquarium water (pentahydrate)

Formula for copper acetate and formalin treatment

Stock Solution

10% Formalin	100 cc
Cupric Acetate	8 grams
Tris	92 grams

treatment with 1 cc of above stock solution per . 25 gallons of aquarium water.

Copper, in the form of copper sulfate solution, is frequently used to rid the fish of these parasites since the Oodinium is very sensitive to copper. Fish are more tolerant than invertebrates to copper but they have a tendancy to concentrate it after repeated dosages, at which time, a toxic or lethal level is reached. The primary sites of copper concentration in fish are the brain, liver, and ribs. These are the initial areas where an overdose of copper can be observed. Many of these overdosed fish will have sores and lesions on their cranial region and sides. Post mortems of such fish usually reveal necrotic livers.

Certain precautions should be followed in treating Oodinium with copper. The dosage of copper in the aquarium should not exceed .25 ppm at any one time and prolonged treatments, over a week, should be avoided. The copper used for treatment will very quickly become inactive forming a precipitate with the bicarbonates present in the aquarium. This process starts as soon as the copper is introduced, and

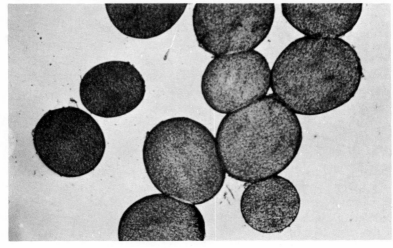

Photomicrograph of *Oodinium* after it has fallen off of its host.
(photo credit: R. Valenti)

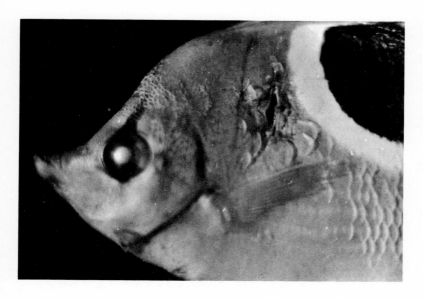

Butterfly fish showing wound on side from an
overdose of copper sulfate.
(photo credit: R. Valenti)

Anesthetics for Marine fishes

MS-222 (Tri-Caine Methanosulfonate), produced by Sandoz Pharmaceuticals, Hanover, N.J., is a very effective drug for narcotizing fishes. The amount of drug to use varies widely with different fish but a .01% solution is highly effective. Care should be taken, since an overdose will cause death.

Quinaldine (2 methylquinoline), produced by Matheson, Coleman and Bell, East Rutherford, N.J. The effective dosage again varies greatly depending upon the particular fish to be narcotized. A dosage of from 5-12 ppm is usually suitable. Fish should stop moving in about 1-3 minutes if the dosage is correct.

within a day approximately 30% of the copper is already out of solution. For this reason treatment should be extended over a two or three day period. During this time enough copper will remain active to kill the Oodinium but not enough will be concentrated by the fish to affect them adversely. There are several copper test kits available which will give an accurate measure of copper in the aquarium. Remember, a .10 ppm - .15 ppm concentration should be maintained for three days. This can be achieved by adding copper solution when necessary. Unfortunately, after three days, the amount of copper concentrated by the fish could be lethal. Copper indicators are able to detect only the amount of copper left in the aquarium, they cannot indicate the amount of copper absorbed by the fish.

Many commercially manufactured copper solutions use citric acid in small quantities to prevent precipitation of copper. The copper, regardless of the citric acid, will start to precipitate in the presence of bicarbonates found in the marine aquarium but it will not precipitate out of a stock solution using distilled water.

Feeding live brine shrimp to fish being treated with copper should be avoided since the brine shrimp concentrate copper and when they, in turn, are ingested, a lethal amount of copper is incorporated by the fish (Herald and Dempster, 1965).

The treatment of an aquarium with devices such as a penny or a pieces of copper tubing should be avoided. Needless to say, these devices do not control the amount of copper and an overdose can easily result. In such cases not only lethal amounts of copper enter the water but also much of the bicarbonates are utilized causing a shift in the pH of the water; from the favorable alkaline condition to an unfavorable acidic condition.

The use of copper acetate has proved to be a much more efficient form of copper than is the copper sulfate, since it will not precipate out of solution as quickly. It has been my experience, however, that more fish die from an overdose of copper than from Oodinium and for this reason the use of copper acetate is not recommended for the average aquarist.

Care should be taken to remove all plants and invertebrates from the aquarium before adding any copper. These organisms are far more sensitive to copper, than are the fish, and will quickly perish even in minute concentrations of copper.

This author has had success in treating Oodinium by using a newly developed technique. The diseased fish are individually anesthetized (MS222) and placed in a small container of concentrated copper, at least 100 ppm, for approximately thirty seconds. Since the fish's

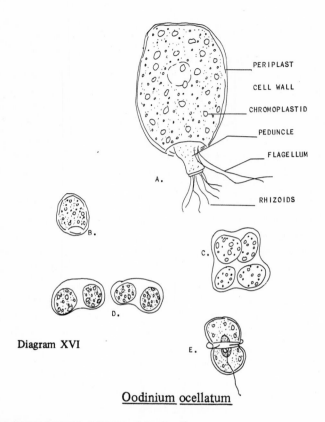

Diagram XVI

Labels on figure A:
PERIPLAST
CELL WALL
CHROMOPLASTID
PEDUNCLE
FLAGELLUM
RHIZOIDS

<u>Oodinium ocellatum</u>

STAGES IN LIFE CYCLE: (abridged)

A.   Parasitic—attached to fish gill or body,
                    —Copper treatment effective

B-C.   Palmella—Occurs from two to five minutes after leaving fish.
                    swells up by taking in water, starts dividing
                    —Copper treatment effective.

D-E.   Dinospore—(app. after 128-256 cells) Naked dinospores have
                    a free swimming stage. They go to the bottom once
                    more to secrete a new cellulose covering (peridinian
                    dinoflagellate) before being truly free swimming.
                    After they are free swimming, they attach to fish and
                    become the parasitic stage.

The life cycle is effected by salinity and temperature.

metabolic rate is reduced by the anesthetic, much of the copper is not absorbed but yet it does bathe the gills and the exterior of the body, and in this way the Oodinium is removed.

Since the parasites may never be present on the surface of the body, knowing when to treat fish for Oodinium can be difficult. Oodinium receives some nutrients by attaching to the mucus secretion on the surface of the fish. The main source of its nutrition, however, is from the capillary laden gill filaments (Nigrelli, 1935). For this reason many fish will be heavily parasitized and exhibit no external evidence of it, since the parasites are attached to the gill filaments. The symptoms most often associated with Oodinium infection are the constant scratching of the fish against rocks or coral and rapid breathing. Unfortunately, these symptons may also be indicative of other disorders such as an overdose of copper. As a precautionary measure, new arrivals into an aquarium should be pre-treated. If such a practice is followed the incidence of infection will be greatly reduced.

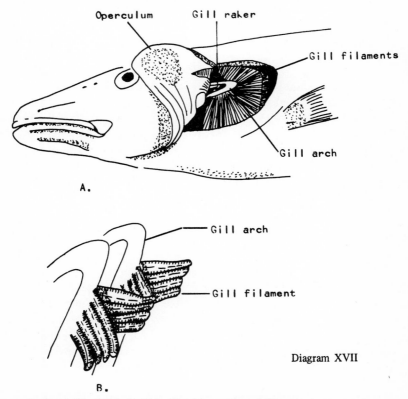

Diagram XVII

A. Exposed gill of fish showing gill rakers, arch and filaments.
B. Closer view of gill filaments and their attachment to the supporting gill arch.

Torn dorsal fin on this file fish should
not be confused with dorsal fin-rot.
This is merely due to improper handling
of the fish in a net. (photo credit: R. Valenti)

Gill Copepods

There are a number of common parasitic copepods (Arthropods) which attach to the gills of fish. Some copepods are equipped with two large hooks. These hooks are the means by which they firmly attach to the various surfaces of the fish. When these claspers are driven into the gill filaments, the copepods almost become permanent attachments. In severe cases, a large number of these copepods will block the exchange of gases in the gills and suffocation results. Treatment with .15 ppm of copper sulfate will eliminate this parasite effectively.

Air Embolism

An overabundance and, too, a lack of oxygen creates physical stresses to which the fish must respond. If the water temperature is extremely high, 82-85° F., and air is rapidly bubbled under pressure through a fine airstone, the fish's circulatory fluids may become oversaturated with oxygen. Gas bubbles can form in the main circulatory vessels and thus create a physical barrier to the passage of blood, thus normal circulation is hindered and death may ensue. Often in such cases the fish will manifest slight eruptions under the skin and on the fins. If the fish is placed into fresh sea water with a lower concentration of dissolved gases, complete recovery may soon follow if irreparable damage has not already occurred.

Ichthyophthirius marinus (Cryptocaryon irritans)

White spot disease of marine fish is the counterpart of the fresh water disease, Ichthyophthirius multifiliis. This ciliated protozoa is mainly a gill parasite but does attack the skin often. When the parasite becomes numerous on the gills, excessive mucus is secreted blocking effective respiration and causing a condition known as histiophagus. White spot disease can be effectively treated by placing ill fish in a 5% solution of methylene blue for one week.

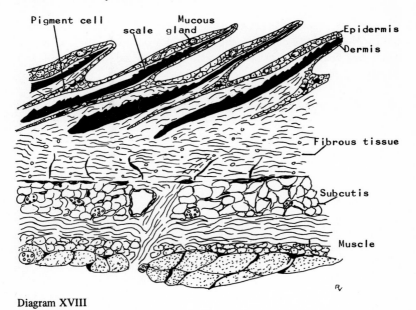

Diagram XVIII

Section of fish skin (source General Biological Supply House).

SKIN INFECTIONS AND PARASITES

The superficial layers of fish's skin are: the epidermis, (the outermost layer,) and the dermis. The epidermis contains mucous glands that secrete the slime which covers the scales of the fish. Fish differ in the relative thickness of secreted slime layers; parrot fish, for example, have a great deal of slime which provides a certain protection against bacterial infections and bruises. Generally, the more slime a fish has the better its chances against parasitic invasion of surface layers. Upon occasion, either stress or toxic substances will cause an increase of mucus secretion which will not slough off but will accumulate and thereby support the existence of large bacterial populations. The bacteria, while not harmful alone, may provide a source of additional nutrition for marine ciliates (Protozoa) which in high enough numbers can be a source of irritation and may be the cause of ulcerated wounds. This series of events culminates in a phenomenon called Epibiosis. This interplay of circumstances clarifies the interdependence of organisms in a restricted environment.

The dermis is rich in blood vessels and connective tissue. The scales are positioned and secured within pockets in the dermis and are partially covered with a layer of connective tissue overlaid with epidermis. The chromatophores, or pigment cells, that give the fish its characteristic colors, lie between the dermis and the epidermis. When the chromatophores contract, the fish's color becomes less intense and when they relax the color becomes greatly intensified.

Bacterial Infections

Bacterial infections of existing wounds or bruises, called secondary bacterial infections, are a frequent occurrence, but to eliminate all bacteria from the tank is harmful if not impossible. Bacteria usually live on the surface and in internal organs (for example in the digestive tract) of fish and are essential to their survival. Once a fish becomes bruised

A new arrival may often "go into shock" from increased stress.
(photo credit: R. Valenti)

146

Acanthurus xanthopterus, showing cut spine to
prevent damage during shipping. Unfortunately,
this can often do more damage then it prevents.
(photo credit: R. Valenti)

Bruises inflicted during shipping.
Top left and right, *C. vagabundus,* bottom left,
C. vagabundus, bottom right, *C. speculum.*
(photo credit: R. Valenti)

either by attack from another tank inhabitant or through improper handling, bacterial infections can occur. These symptons include red, swollen sores, white blotches on the surface of the fish, and even deteriorating fins ("fin-rot"). Treatment of open sores and wounds as well as deteriorating fins is best accomplished by swabbing the infected area with a 1% solution (1 gram of compound added to 100ml of solution) of Malachite green. Acriflavine, a compound often used in aquariums, can also be applied similarly, by swabbing with a 1% solution. (cotton tipped splinters make efficient swabs). Treating "blotch infections" on the surface of the fish is best accomplished by antibiotic dips. Indiscriminate use of any antibiotic should be discouraged and avoided as it will cause the bloom of antibiotic-resistant strains of bacteria. If the cause of the problem can be diagnosed definitely as a bacterial infection, then, and only then, should antibiotics be used. Since a mixture of several antibiotics is more effective than any single antibiotic and since total effectiveness of the antibiotic, once in solution, is only several hours (depending upon the particular antibiotic), dipping the fish into an antibiotic mixture is best. If fish are bruised or have open sores, a good preventive measure, before placing them in a community tank, is to dip them in the antibiotic solution for one minute. The fish can be restricted in the net and then plunged into the mix.

ANTIBIOTIC MIX
(mix antibiotics fresh before using)
total volume 2 gallons

200 mg Penicillin
200 mg Chloromycetin
200 mg Streptomycin

The use of sodium chlorite to keep down bacterial populations as well as a prophylatic measure to control protozoan diseases, has been investigated at several public aquaria. Sodium chlorite at 2.0-5.0 ppm appears to inhibit bacteria and some protozoa, while at this low concentration it does not inhibit bacterial filtration or become toxic to most fish and invertebrates. It should be remembered that since this is a strong oxidizing agent care must be taken not to use too much of it at one time or treat too often. It would appear that further experimentation with this compound is worth while to the aquarist but it must not be used indiscriminately.

Formulation for sodium chlorite

grams of sodium chlorite (80%) = $\dfrac{V\ 6.34\ ppm}{1000}$

V = gallons of aquarium water to be treated
6.34 = a constant
ppm = concentration desired

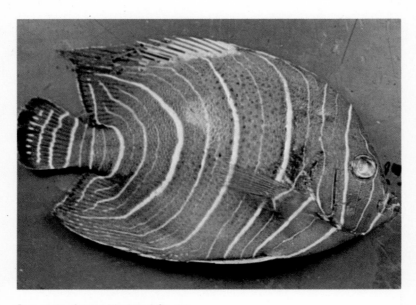

P. semicirculatus with dorsal fin rot
(photo credit: R. Valenti)

P. arcuatus with tail rot
(photo credit: R. Valenti)

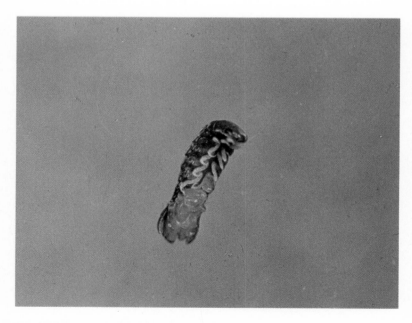

External copepod frequently found on coral
reef fish. (photo credit: R. Valenti)

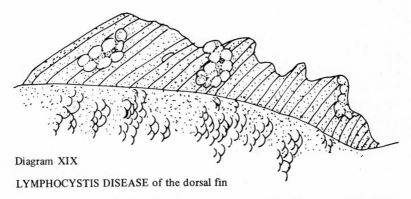

Diagram XIX

LYMPHOCYSTIS DISEASE of the dorsal fin

Oppenheimer (1955) developed the use of penicillin-G and Strepto-mycin sulfate for keeping down bacterial populations on pelagic eggs. The dosage he used is highly effective while not damaging even delicate larval fishes.

| Penicillin – G | 50 I.U./ml |
| Streptomycin sulfate | .05 mg/ml |

This dosage should be added to a small quarantine tank (app. 5 gallons which contain 20,000 ml of water). It will not be effective after 72 hours.

Fungus Infections

Fungus infections occur frequently and simultaneously with bacterial infections. They can be distinguished from bacterial infections since the infected area is fuzzy due to the tufted filaments or hyphae that project from the surface of the infection. Infections are usually localized to small areas which makes treatment easy by simply touching or swabbing the area with a 1% solution of Malachite green. The prevalent fungus, Ichthyophonus hoferi, is a pathogen of marine fish which causes lesions of the brain and heart. Dipping infected fish in a 1% solution of Malachite green for 60 seconds will minimize infections in the early stages.

Viral Infections

Perhaps the most prevalent viral disease is Lymphocystis. The virus causing the infection stimulates an hypertropy, or an increase in growth, of the connective tissue cells, with the result that these cells become enormous in size, sometimes reaching a total diameter of one millimeter. These enlarged cells are usually white and appear clumpy. Treatment of the disease is still at the experimental level. The infectious virus has been found to be resistant to potassium hydroxide, and glycerin but sensitive to ether. If the enlarged cells are attached to the fins merely pulling them off with a forceps is effective. Since secondary fungus infections occur concurrently, swabbing with a 1% Malachite-green solution is helpful. Once this disease occurs in the aquarium, the infected fish should be removed and treated in a quarantine tank. The isolation of infected fish will prevent spreading of disease to the other fish.

Papilloma diseases commonly found in many species of inshore marine fishes are caused by an infectious virus. The disease is prevalent in young fishes, although outbreaks of papilloma tumors have been reported in adult male slippery dicks (T. bifasciatus).

Infectious dropsy, a disease caused by infected kidneys and subsequent accumulation of fluids in the body cavity, is sometimes caused by viruses. It may also be caused by bacteria which produce symptoms similar to those of viral origin. The fish's abdomen will swell and the scales covering this area will stick out at a perpendicular angle to the skin. Removal to new water may help.

External Copepods

Many marine fish are parasitized by copepods which are able to grasp the skin of the fish at the same time injecting into the fish an anti-coagulant and then remove vital body fluids through the small wounds they cause. These parasites are readily visible upon examination.

If the fish is removed from the tank and restricted in a net either carefully placing a drop of alcohol on the parasite or prying it loose with forceps will eliminate the source of irritation for the fish.

INTERNAL PARASITES

Platyhelminthes and Nematoda

Marine fish are usually heavily infested with trematodes (flukes), nematodes (round worms) and cestodes (tapeworms). The aquarist can do little, however, to remove them since diagnosis is difficult and the areas of infection are internal and would require surgery. While many fish are parasitized by these organisms, death is usually not a direct cause of their presence. Fish which are heavily parasitized by these organisms will often succumb when exposed to stress such as being moved to a new aquarium. Those parasites which encyst in the flesh of fish can be seen as nodules or lumps beneath the skin. Benedenia sp. is a monogenetic trematode commonly parasitizing aquarium fishes. They often attach to the eyes, gills and nasal cavities of infected fish. Benedenia can be controlled by lowering the water temperature to 65° F., which is below their optimal living temperature of 72°F. The use of

C. ornatissimus showing lesion caused by
encysted nematode
(photo credit: R. Valenti)

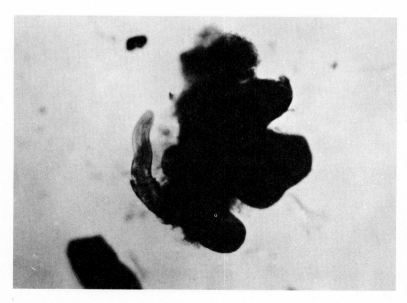

Nematode found in musculature of butterfly fish
(photo credit: R. Valenti)

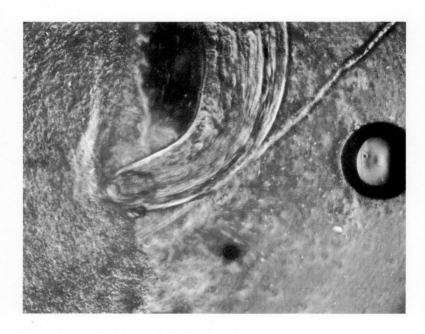

Photomicrograph of nematode in intestine of
A. percula, showing head region of parasite.
(photo credit: R. Valenti)

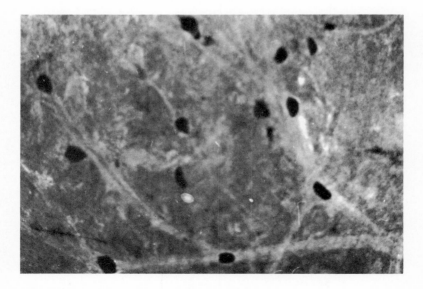

Spleen of fish showing microsporidean infection
(photo credit: R. Valenti)

Photomicrograph of a myxosporidean spore
(photo credit: R. Valenti)

F. heteroclitus, with kidney infection causing build-up
of fluids
(photo credit: R. Valenti)

di-n-butyl tin oxide has been found to be effective in treating internal infections of cestodes and nematodes. The treatment is added to the fish's food in a liquid form over a three day period.

Stock Solution of di-n-butyl tin oxide (mix fresh prior to treatment)

.1 gram of di-n-butyl tin oxide is added to 100 cc of distilled water.

2 drops of this solution are added to the food of the fish every day for three days. This should be effective in treating 3-4 inch fish. For larger fish use proportionately greater concentrations. Be careful when treating fish since an overdose will be damaging to the fish.

Myxosporidea and Microsporidea

During the principle part of their life cycle, sporozoans are amoeboid and lack a macronucleus. There are several modes of reproduction leading to the formation of the infective sporozoite. External symptoms of sporozoan diseases if manifested at all, are in the form of white pimple-like eruptions or knots on the sides of the fish. In some isolated cases, open, ulcerated sores are associated with the presence of sporozoan parasites. The parasites attack the ovaries, kidneys, and spleen of their host and death quickly follows. Epidemics can be easily caused if one fish in the aquarium has the disease. Perhaps the most effective treatment for these parasites is quinine sulfate. This compound should be made into stock solution for easy application and treatment.

Quinnine-Sulfate Stock Solution

One gram of quinine sulfate in 100 cc. of acidic water (pH 5-6) will treat 10 gallons of sea water. The solution should be freshly made before each treatment and kept in a dark bottle, as it will break-down from exposure to excessive light. The treatment should be divided over a three day period with equal amounts administered each day.

Quinine will be effective for a relatively long period of time, approximately one month, therefore do not add additional amounts more than once a month. Unfortunately, quinine is not as effective as might be hoped in treating sporozoan infections and it is for this reason that treating only the infected fish by means of quarantine is the recommended procedure. The aquarist might keep in mind that the quinine is the same quinine used in treating malaria and as such it is expense. Quinine has been reported to kill plants as well as interfere with reproduction of fish.

Exophthalmus, "Pop Eye", in a clown fish
(photo credit: R. Valenti)

EYE INFECTIONS (Exophthalmus)

"POP-EYE" is the popular term applied to fish that have a distended or protruding eye or eyes. There are several forms of this disease, each of which is caused by different circumstances: 1.) larvae (a developmental stage in a life cycle) of trematode worms can encyst in the orbit of the eye and cause swelling. 2.) an accumulation of fluids supersaturated with gases can also cause the eye to swell as a result of the expansion of the trapped gas. 3.) a common form of pop-eye is from the accumulation of serous fluids in the tissues of the eye. The cause of fluid accumulation is not really known, however, it has been attributed to microsporidea or bacteria. 4.) often, pop-eye is associated with kidney infections (since the kidneys are responsible for the internal balance of fluids). However, diseased kidneys, either lesioned or abscessed, are only one hypothetical reason for exophthalmus.

Treatment of pop-eye is also nebulous since the cause is unknown. However, if the cause is due to trematodes, swabbing the eye with 1% solution of silver nitrate followed by a 1% swabbed application of potassium dichromate should help. (It is important to remember that directly after swabbing with silver nitrate, potassium dichromate follows). This treatment is also beneficial to bacterial caused pop-eye. Some work has been done on exposing the fish's eye to U-V light. While this will ultimately kill bacteria or perhaps other disease causing organisms, it will also damage the cells of the eye. If left unchecked the swollen eyes of the victim will continue to increase in size until they pop-out of the eye socket at which time secondary infections or shock may ultimately cause death. The external protrusion of the eye is compensatory in that it eliminates any pressure on the brain so that the fish may survive.

NON-PARASTIC AILMENTS

The reader should be aware that there are a host of non-parasitic causes for death of marine fish. These include: nutrition, aging, hormonal disfunctions, and environmental factors of temperature, pH, and salinity. Most of these factors have been briefly discussed in the chapter concerning Water Chemistry and Marine Fish.

Units of Measure
1 litre = 1000 millilitres (ml).
1 gallon = 3.785 litres (l).
1 gram = 15.432 grains (gr).
.1% solution = .1 gram placed in 100 ml.
1% solution = 1 gram placed in 100 ml.
10% solution = 10 grams placed in 100 ml.

FISH DISEASES
BIBLIOGRAPHY

Davis, H.S. 1953. *Culture and Diseases of Game Fishes,* University of California Press, Los Angeles, 332 p.

Dogel, V.A., G. Petrushevski and Y. Polyanski. 1961. *Parasitology of Fishes,* Oliver and Boyd, Edinburgh, 384 p.

Herald, E. and R. Dempster. 1965. Brine Shrimp vs. copper solution, The Aquarium Journal, 36 (7) p. 334.

Nigrelli, R. 1935. The morphology, cytology and life history of *Oodinium ocellatum,* Brown, a dinoflagellate parasite on marine fishes Zoologica, 21 (12) p. 129-164.

Nigrelli, R. and Ruggieri, G. 1965. Studies on virus diseases of fishes spontaneous and experimentally induced cellular hypertrophy (Lymphocystis diseases) in fishes of the New York Aquarium, with a report of new cases and annoted bibliography, Zoologica, 50 (20) p. 83-96.

Reichenback, H., J. Klinke and E. Kan. 1965. *The Principal diseases of Lower Vertebrates,* Academic Press.

Sindermann, Carl. 1966. Diseases of marine fishes *In: Advances in Marine Biology,* Sir Frederick S. Russell (editor), Academic Press, New York, p. 1-89.

Van Duijn, C., Jr. 1967. *Diesease of Fishes,* Water Life, Dorset House, London, 174 p.

Preservation of Specimens

There is little doubt that even the most experienced aquarist will lose a specimen or two during his endeavors. While often as not the aquarist is compelled to dispose of the carcass and let time heal the thought of the mishap; there are those aquarists who feel a preserved specimen is better than none at all. It is for these persons that I include the following outline for preserving fish.

1. An incision (using scissors) should be made in the abdomen of the fish and the internal organs removed.

2. The fish should be rinsed off under fresh water and the excess slime removed. Swabbing the fish with a vinegar soaked piece of cotton will remove the slime.

3. The fish can then be placed into the fixing solution. The choice of solutions varies greatly although the aim of having a solution which will not bleach the coloration from the specimen remains constant. The following solution has been used by the author and works well:

    87 parts .... 70% alcohol
    3 parts .... Glacial Acetic Acid
    10 parts .... Glycerin

4. The specimens should be stored in a tightly capped bottle with the name of the specimen written in ink or wax crayon on the cover. Using waterproof ink on an index card and then placing the card in the solution is a widely used method.

5. When preserving invertebrates, a less acidic solution (add ½ as much glacial acetic acid) should be used to avoid decalcification.

6. Anti-oxidant components, such as IONOL CP-40 (manufactured by the Shell Chemical Co.), added to the above solution will give superior color retention to fixed specimencts. (Waller, R. and W. Eschmeyer 1965, A method for preserving color in biological specimens. BioScience, 15 (5), 361).

INDEX